The Management
of Technical Programs

PRAEGER SPECIAL STUDIES IN
INTERNATIONAL ECONOMICS AND DEVELOPMENT

The Management of Technical Programs

WITH SPECIAL REFERENCE TO THE NEEDS OF DEVELOPING COUNTRIES

LAWRENCE W. BASS

Prepared by
Arthur D. Little, Inc.

FREDERICK A. PRAEGER, Publishers
New York · Washington · London

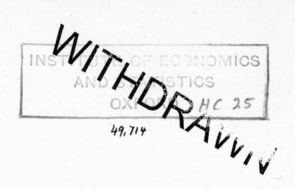
The purpose of the Praeger Special Studies is to make specialized research monographs in international economics and politics available to the academic, business, and government communities. For further information, write to the Special Projects Division, Frederick A. Praeger, Publishers, 111 Fourth Ave., New York, N.Y. 10003.

FREDERICK A. PRAEGER, *Publishers*
111 Fourth Avenue, New York 3, N.Y., U.S.A.
77-79 Charlotte Street, London W.1, England

Published in the United States of America in 1965
by Frederick A. Praeger, Inc., Publishers

Library of Congress Catalog Card Number: 65-16654

Printed in the United States of America

CONTENTS

		Page
List of Tables		xii
List of Figures		xiii
INTRODUCTION		1

1 RESEARCH IN INTERNATIONAL PERSPECTIVE — 3

Recognition of Research as a National Resource — 3
Research in the United States — 3
Research in Western Europe — 4
Research and Development Effort of Various Countries — 5

2 MANAGERIAL PRINCIPLES FOR TECHNICAL PROGRAMS — 7

Basic Considerations — 7
Magnitude of Program — 8
Background for Technical Programs — 8
Planning Objectives and Criteria — 10
Outlining the Technical Program — 11
Organization and Administration — 11
Coordination with Other Departments — 12
Programs for Sectors of Industry — 12
Technical Programming on a National Basis — 13

3 TECHNOLOGIC NEEDS OF DEVELOPING ECONOMIES — 15

Resource Utilization in National Perspective — 15
Criteria for Evaluating Projects — 16
Utilization of Natural Resources — 16
Initial Steps for Using Technical Resources — 17
Introductory Stages of Technical Programs — 19

v

3   TECHNOLOGIC NEEDS OF DEVELOPING ECONOMIES (cont.)

Utilizing Wastes and By-Products   20

Obtaining New Technology from Abroad   21

Assessment of Resources of Technical Manpower   21

Census of Technical Activities   22

4   CHARACTERIZATION AND RELATIONSHIPS OF TECHNICAL
     FUNCTIONS   24

Definitions of Technical Functions   24

Relationships Among Technical Functions   26

5   CORPORATE LOGISTICS AND PRODUCT POLICY   29

The Life Cycle of Technology   29

Characterization of "New Products"   29

Formulation of Product Policy   33

Assessment of Corporate Resources for Undertaking New
Products   34

Responsibilities of New Product Planning   35

Management of Product Suggestion Systems   36

6   ELEMENTS OF TECHNICAL PROGRAMMING   38

Scope of Managerial Responsibilities   38

Analysis of Program and Technical Resources   38

Project Systems as a Control Procedure   39

Mortality of Research Ideas   40

Evaluation and Abandonment of Projects   41

Specialized Functions of Other Departments   41

Analysis of Total Program   43

Page

7   ORGANIZATION OF TECHNICAL DEPARTMENTS   44

     Purpose of an Organization   44
     Formal Plan of Organization   45
     Technical Coordination Committees   48
     Echelons in Technical Organizations   50
     The Informal Working Organization   50
     Extra-Mural Research Projects   51

8   BASIC RESEARCH   53

     Fundamental Research in Academic Institutions   53
     Sponsored Research in American Universities   53
     Postgraduate Training in Developing Economies   54
     Basic Research in American Industry   55
     Serendipity in Basic Research   56
     Oriented Long-Range Research   57
     Oriented Long-Range Research in Developing Countries   58

9   PRODUCT AND PROCESS DEVELOPMENT   59

     Stages and Steps in Development   59
     Basic Research   60
     Applied Research   60
     Product Development   61
     Process Development and Field Evaluation   63
     Pilot Plant Operation and Market Tests   64
     Comprehensive Review Preparatory to Commercialization   66
     Initial Steps for Commercialization   67
     Implementation of Commercial Project   67

		Page
10	ENGINEERING DEVELOPMENT FUNCTIONS	69
	Scope and Coordination	69
	Definitions of Engineering Functions	69
	Step-Wise Process Development	70
	Pilot Plants as Small-Scale Production Units	71
	Process Engineering	72
	Techno-economic Evaluation	72
	Project Engineering	73
11	COORDINATION OF TECHNOLOGY WITH MANUFACTURING	74
	Quality Control	74
	Quality Control Programs for Central Laboratories	75
	Use of Quality Control in Productivity Studies	75
	Technical Service to Manufacturing	76
	Maintenance Planning and Preventive Maintenance	76
	Economic Balance in Selecting Process and Equipment	77
	Other Engineering Functions	77
12	COORDINATION OF TECHNOLOGY WITH MARKETING	78
	Technical Service to Marketing	78
	Service to Marketing for Export Items and Consumer Products	79
	Sample Preparation for the Trade	80
	Determination of Properties	80
	Application Research	80
	Complaints	81
	Analysis of Competition	81

12   COORDINATION OF TECHNOLOGY WITH MARKETING (cont.)

      Market Research   82
      Consumer Research   83

13   PROJECT SYSTEMS   84

      Rationale of Project Systems   84
      Project Outlines   84
      Minor Assignments   85
      Continuing Projects   87
      Overhead Projects   87
      Review of Program   88
      Project Assignments   89
      Procedures for Installing Project Systems   89
      Budgeting Control Procedures   90

14   TECHNICAL TASK FORCES   92

      Multi-Discipline Approach   92
      Advantages of Task Force Systems   92
      Illustrative Case History of Task Force Operation   93
      Corporate Coordination of Task Forces   96
      How to Introduce Task Force Operations   98

15   COORDINATION OF CORPORATE DEVELOPMENT FUNCTIONS   102

      Corporate Planning   102
      Corporate Development Functions   103
      Job Description of a Director of Corporate Development   105

15   COORDINATION OF CORPORATE DEVELOPMENT FUNCTIONS
     (cont.)

          Relationship of Corporate Development to the Technical
          Department   107

          Use of Corporate Objectives in Technical Programming   108

16   CASE HISTORY OF A TECHNICAL PROGRAM   109

          General Principles   109

          Economic Background of the Enterprise   109

          Planning the Technical Program   111

          Program and Work Assignments   114

          Program and Budget Preparation for 1965   114

          Revision of the Technical Program   116

          Estimation of Activities to Commercialize Product H   117

17   COMMERCIAL DEVELOPMENT AS A MEASURE OF CORPORATE
     TECHNOLOGY   21

          Background   121

          Analysis and Projection of Technical Contributions to
          Profitability   121

          Classification of Added Products   123

          Historical Analysis of Added Products   124

          Methodology for Forecasting   127

          Use of APTeC in Evaluating Corporate Technical Postures 129

18   SUMMARY OF ADMINISTRATIVE PRINCIPLES   131

          General Objectives of Technical Administration   131

          Personnel Administration   132

Page

18   SUMMARY OF ADMINISTRATIVE PRINCIPLES (cont.)

        Reports   133
        Program Review   134
        Operating Budgets and Accounting   135
        Capital Expenditure Budgets   136
        Purchasing for Technical Departments   137
        Library and Information Service   137
        Conclusion   138

ABOUT THE AUTHOR   139

LIST OF TABLES

Table
No.   Page

1   Expenditure for Research and Development in Various
      Countries   6

2   Research and Development Expenditure as a Proportion of
      Net Output and of Sales in Various Industries in Selected
      Countries, 1958 and 1959   9

3   Benefits and Risks of New Items, New Products, and New
      Product Lines   31

4   Criteria for Classification of Added Products   32

5   Task Force for New Breakfast Food   94

6   1964 Program and Manpower Allocations Before Considering
      Vinyl Acetate Expansion   112

7   Cost of Research and Development Per Scientist or Engineer   113

8   1965 Revised Program and Manpower Allocations to Provide
      for Expanded Polyvinyl Acetate Work   118

9   Technical-Man-Year Schedule to Commercialize Polyvinyl
      Acetate (Project H)   120

10   Past Benefits Versus Technical Expense   126

11   Projection of Sales and Profits Versus Technical Expense
      of Added Products   128

LIST OF FIGURES

Figure No.		Page
1	The Technologic Pyramid	27
2	Technical Manpower Involved in a Typical Project	42
3	Organization Chart of a Small Company	46
4	Organization Chart of a Medium-Sized Company	47
5	Organization Chart of a Large Company	49
6	Project Outline	86
7	Project Coordination Chart	99

The Management of Technical Programs

INTRODUCTION

In the course of a few decades, the rapid march of technologic innovation has created an acceptance of continual change in the industrial economy as the natural course of events. Hence, the problem of making optimum use of technical resources is a major concern of all companies, industries, and nations. Intensive study of the management of research, development, and engineering is being carried out in industrialized countries. The subject is of even greater importance in developing economies: their need for technologic progress is great, their technical reservoirs are limited.

This monograph is addressed to the analysis of policies and procedures for bringing scientists and engineers into productive action to solve practical problems. It is based on the syllabus prepared for a training course on "Management of Science and Technology in Developing Economies"which was conducted by an ADL team in Cairo during a three-week period in the spring of 1964 under the auspices of the Egyptian National Institute of Management Development and The Ford Foundation. The course was given to a group of 38 Egyptian technical executives. There were 40 two-hour sessions, each consisting of a lecture followed by workshop activities of small groups of participants.

The success of this pioneering training program has aroused interest in a number of other developing countries, and it therefore seemed desirable to revise the syllabus for broader readership, incorporating the experience gained through the Cairo presentations. At the same time, because it contains much original material on the management of technical activities, it should be of general interest to those concerned with the translation of science into industrial undertakings.

It should be axiomatic that the details of organization and management techniques in one case are not necessarily transferable directly to another set of conditions. The emphasis in this publication is intended to be on basic principles, and the illustrative examples of procedures are offered, not in dogmatic spirit, but only to clarify typical procedures for implementing the underlying considerations.

It is a happy circumstance that this first training course of the kind was under the aegis of an organization such as the National Institute of Management Development. This setting gave emphasis to the interdependence of science and business economics, which is a necessary philosophy in developing countries to avoid dissipation of scarce technical talents in unproductive directions. Neither scientist nor economist alone can make balanced judgments of industrial feasibility. When they are intertwined, their logic is indeed much greater than their separate approaches.

The question may arise that discussions of the large organizations and sophisticated managerial practices of industrialized countries are hardly appropriate in less developed areas. This objection was not encountered in the Cairo course, because some of the larger technical organizations in industry are sizable, and particularly because centralized government agencies encounter comparable problems. In any case, much of the literature on research management refers to advanced techniques used in big departments, so that evaluation of the extent to which they may be applicable in less complicated situations will lead to better use of the published material on the subject.

Since in many developing countries industry is under government control to a greater or less extent, the differences between operations in the public sector and those in the private sector should not be a handicap in discussing the management of technical programs. The ultimate purpose in both cases is to use science and technology to enhance the return to the economy. To be truly successful, each must develop a prosperous, self-sustaining operation which satisfies consumer needs, provides employment, and contributes to the welfare of the nation. In private enterprises, the economic return is in the form of profits, which are used as capital for improved or expanded operations, and as income to shareholders, from whom it passes into the general economy by various routes. In public enterprises, the return that is generated is used as capital needed for expansion of the particular operation or as a direct or indirect--e.g., conservation of foreign exchange--contribution to the national treasury.

CHAPTER 1 — RESEARCH IN INTERNATIONAL PERSPECTIVE

Recognition of Research as a National Resource

In recent decades research has achieved the prestige of a major resource for national well-being and progress. Its importance is endorsed by
governments and by managers of industrial enterprises. This endorsement is
expressed in tangible form by the huge sums being spent in support of technical
programs by individual companies, by industry groups, and by government
agencies.

Recognition of science by public and private organizations stems from
acceptance of the doctrine of continual change. Hence a nation or an industrial
firm must, in order to maintain a healthy status inside the country and in international affairs, establish procedures for encouraging an orderly process of
change in its own operations.

Science and technology even a century ago began to overcome geographical boundaries through improved communications. Today the rate of growth of
scientific information is astounding, and the individual scientist finds it difficult
to keep up-to-date on all that is going on in his specialized field. All nations and
industrial organizations have access to this world reservoir of knowledge insofar
as they develop proper channels for obtaining, screening, evaluating, adapting,
and implementing the information.

Organized scientific research on industrial problems gained momentum
about a century ago through its success in Germany in the evolution of the synthetic chemical industry. It spread gradually through the Western world and laid
the foundation for the technologic progress that led to the establishment of many
large enterprises in the science-based industries. At the end of World War I
enhanced recognition of its potential encouraged more rapid strides.

Research in the United States

In the United States the number of research laboratories began to increase notably, from 290 in 1920 to 5420 in 1960, according to one authoritative
listing. At present nearly all companies of large or medium size consider it
essential to have an organized research and development activity. The research
director is often a member of the top management team. The financial community
considers technical strength as an important factor in evaluating growth potential
of a company.

Technical innovation has resulted in increasing use of scientists and engineers in industry, not only in research and development, but also in production, distribution, and various staff and management positions. The use of science and engineering by Government agencies has also increased greatly during and since World War II. Today 2.7 million people in the United States, representing 3.6% of the labor force, are scientists, engineers, technicians, or science teachers, and by 1970 the number is expected to grow to four million, 4.7% of the labor force.

In terms of cost, the total research and development expenditures in the United States have grown from $2.5 billion in 1950 to an estimated $20 billion in 1964, equivalent to 2.8% of gross national product. This latter figure breaks down into $14 billion to be spent by the Federal Government (of which $9 billion will be used for projects carried out in industrial organizations), $5.5 billion spent by industry, and $0.5 billion by universities and institutions. It is estimated that about 400,000 scientists and engineers are engaged in research and development.

Research and development activities have become such a potent factor in the American economy that they are often said to constitute a separate industry. Statistics are being collected on an elaborate scale. Management techniques and problems are being discussed in symposia and publications. Major problems receiving particular attention are: measurement of research and development effectiveness (for which there is yet no accepted procedure), greater speed in applying new knowledge commercially, and greater creativity.

There is a growing belief in the United States and in Europe, shared by industry and Government, that the total research effort is approaching a plateau. Expansion of technical programs has been so rapid that it does indeed appear that there must be a reasonable limit to the number of competent researchers and to the ability of the economy to support and make proper application of scientific and technologic developments. Emphasis is therefore on raising the level of quality, and in industry, more incisive analysis of projects in order to ensure greater utility to the company, including more effective use of the vast store of information already available.

Research in Western Europe

In Europe the pace of research and development is also increasing rapidly. There has been a stronger tendency toward Government encouragement than in the United States. This was spear-headed by the cooperative research idea in France at the turn of the century and by the establishment of industrial research association laboratories in the United Kingdom after World War I, supported in part by Government and in part by industry. Many other countries have followed a similar course. This is in contrast to the situation in America, where association laboratories have played a minor role; instead, independent contract organizations, conducting specific projects for individual companies or agencies, have grown up, and this movement has been spreading in recent years in Europe. In certain countries, notably Germany and Switzerland, a very successful policy has been followed for close cooperation between industry and the technical universities.

The larger European companies in science-based industries conduct research and development on a scale similar to that found in America, and indeed their contributions to industrial technology are most impressive. Until recently, however, there has been little systematic effort to collect information about the magnitude of national research and little in the published literature on management of technical programs.

The Organization for Economic Co-operation and Development, an intergovernmental agency with 18 member nations, is performing a notable service in collecting, analyzing, and publishing information on technical activities. Its recent report on "Science, Economic Growth, and Government Policy" should be in the library of everyone interested in the broad implications of scientific progress. The major subjects in this publication are: knowledge and economic growth, international trends in research and development, factors affecting research and development activity, research and development in the business enterprise sector, the place of government in research and development, government policy toward business enterprises, some general aspects of a science policy, and the priorities of a science policy for economic growth.

Research and Development Effort of Various Countries

Considerable effort is being directed toward comparison of the scientific and technologic postures of various countries. Information for this purpose is by no means adequate or comparable. The data suffice, however, for order-of-magnitude evaluation of the extent to which science is being employed in socio-economic development.

A recent article "Measuring the Growth of Science" by Stevan Dedijier of Sweden (Science, 138, No. 3542, pp.781-788, November 16, 1962) gives a very interesting analysis of the problem and provides the figures given in Table 1, condensed from one of his tables, from information collected for the period 1958-61. Obviously data reported by different countries are not on a basis that permits quantitative conclusions, but it is to be hoped that in coming years there will be improvements in the figures available. Additional data about the status of research in international perspective are given in the O.E.C.D. report mentioned in the preceding section.

TABLE 1

EXPENDITURE FOR RESEARCH AND DEVELOPMENT
IN VARIOUS COUNTRIES

Country	R&D Expenditure as Percentage of Gross National Product	R&D Expenditure per Inhabitant (U.S. $)	Consumption of Commercial Energy per Inhabitant (kg equivalent of coal)
United States	2.8	78.4	8013
U.S.S.R.	2.3 (?)	36.4	2847
United Kingdom	2.5	26.0	4920
Sweden	1.8	24.3	3496
Canada	1.2	21.9	5679
West Germany	1.4	15.7	3651
France	1.3	15.2	2402
Norway	0.7	10.0	2732
Australia	0.6	8.9	3904
Japan	1.6	6.2	1164
New Zealand	0.3	5.3	1982
Poland	0.9 (?)	5.3 (?)	3097
Yugoslavia	0.7	1.4	858
China	-	0.6	600
Ghana	0.2	0.4	98
Lebanon	0.1	0.3	596
Egypt	-	0.3	281
Philippines	0.1	<0.3	138
India	0.1	<0.1	140
Pakistan	0.1	<0.1	67

CHAPTER **2**   MANAGERIAL
PRINCIPLES FOR
TECHNICAL PROGRAMS

Basic Considerations

The following principles should govern the formulation of a technical
program:

1. The most valuable asset for research and development is the col-
    lective talent of the technical staff, and therefore all matters of
    organization, policies, coordination, and working conditions
    should have as their objective the stimulation of scientific and
    engineering personnel to perform at their optimum level of ability.

2. A basic philosophy should be established to define the purpose,
    goals, character, organizational relationships, size, and financial
    support, preferably on a projected time scale.

3. The guiding policy in administering work assignments to members
    of the technical staff should be to give them a well-rounded orienta-
    tion on the purpose and importance of each project in order that
    they may feel personal involvement and responsibility, and to keep
    them informed of any changing background that has a bearing on
    the goals or significance of their contributions.

4. Each situation--whether corporate, industry-wide, or national--
    requires its particular solution. Organizations and procedures
    that prove successful in one case may be inappropriate in other
    conditions because of differences in objectives, organization, per-
    sonnel, cultural background, resources, state of technology,
    competitive factors, etc.

5. Because there are no yardsticks for measuring research produc-
    tivity, there is no hard-and-fast basis for deciding what type of
    organization and program should be established. Hence, the col-
    lective experience of others, when properly analyzed, provides
    valuable background for meeting a given situation.

6. Some technical activity is essential in practically all enterprises,
    except smaller undertakings based on the older industrial arts,
    merely to maintain the operation in good performance. Even in
    advanced technologies this type of service or short-term develop-
    ment to maintain competitive position usually accounts for a major
    part of the technical program. It should be recognized for what it
    is--the cost of staying in business--and should not be confused with
    innovative research and development aimed at improved industrial
    status.

7

7. Technology does not stand still. A highly satisfactory operation, such as a successful turn-key plant, sooner or later requires research and development to ensure its long-term survival. The new technology required is difficult to generate on a crash basis, and plans to provide it should be matured before urgent need.

8. A research and development organization can rarely be expanded effectively at a rate greater than 20-25 percent per year, because recruiting, indoctrination, work assignment, and supervision represent a heavy drain on technical management. Hence, it is advisable in developing a program to provide a realistic time scale for expansion.

9. The technical director, particularly insofar as he is responsible for new technology as contrasted with day-to-day service, should report to a member of general management, in order that the policy guidance for research and development may reflect broad corporate objectives rather than immediate problems of manufacturing or marketing.

Magnitude of Program

The experience of an industry in the magnitude of technical effort required to keep it viable is helpful as a guide to an individual case. In practice, the figures cited in Table 2 are not to be regarded other than as a general basis for evaluating the needs of a given situation. Research expenditures expressed as proportions of sales are frequently used, of course with the reservation that different companies within the industry may show wide variations. The ratio in terms of "value added" or "net output," a more realistic comparison, is coming into more frequent use.

The data in Table 2 are quoted from the O.E.C.D. publication cited in Chapter I: "Science, Economic Growth, and Government Policy."

Background for Technical Programs

From ADL experience in surveying the technical programs of a large number of industrial organizations in the United States and abroad, four general questions stand out as a basis for evaluating their effectiveness:

TABLE 2

RESEARCH AND DEVELOPMENT EXPENDITURE AS A PROPORTION OF
NET OUTPUT AND OF SALES IN VARIOUS INDUSTRIES
IN SELECTED COUNTRIES, 1958 AND 1959

	Research Expenditure as Percentage of Sales[1] - 1959			Research Expenditure as Percentage of Net Output[2] - 1958		
	Canada	Japan	United States	United States	Sweden	United Kingdom
Group A:						
Aircraft			20.8	30.9		35.1
Electronics	1.8	2.6	12.8	22.4	14.0	12.8
Other Electrical		2.0	10.1	16.3		5.6
Chemicals	1.5	1.9	4.3	6.9[4]	3.2	4.5[4]
Machinery		1.2	4.2	6.3	7.9	2.3
Vehicles	1.9[3]	1.2	3.4	10.2		1.4
Instruments		1.8	8.3	9.9		6.0
Total Group A				13.0	8.3[5]	6.3
Group B:						
Rubber	0.5	1.1	2.0	2.7	2.5	2.1
Ferrous metal	0.4	0.7	0.6	0.8	2.0	0.5
Non-ferrous metals	0.7	1.2	1.0	2.0		2.3
Metal Products		0.9	1.7	1.3		0.8
Stone, clay and glass	0.8	1.2	1.4	1.2	2.0	0.6
Paper	0.4	0.5	0.8	0.9	0.8	0.8
Total Group B				1.3		0.9
Group C:						
Food	0.1	0.4	0.3	0.5	0.5	0.3
Textiles and apparel	1.2	0.7	0.5	0.2	0.5	0.3
Lumber and furniture	0.2	0.3	0.5	0.2	0.6	0.04
Other manufacturing	0.7	0.9	1.4	0.9		0.4
Total Group C				0.5		0.3
Total All Industries	0.7	1.2	4.2	5.7	4.0	3.1

1. Only for firms reporting R&D expenditures.
2. Net output of whole industry including firms not performing R&D. Sweden and
   United States "value added."
3. All transportation equipment.
4. Including petroleum refining.
5. Excluding chemicals.

Note: These data are not strictly comparable between countries because of slight
      differences in industrial classification but they are a good indication of the
      ratios between industries in the same country.

Source: Organization for Economic Cooperation and Development.

1. Has the company management formulated objectives and criteria to carry out an orderly improvement in its operations to reach defined goals?

2. Has the technical manager worked out a comprehensive technical program aimed at using scientific resources to best advantage to aid the enterprise in reaching management's goals?

3. Are the organization and administration of the technical program properly established to produce the scientific and engineering information required?

4. Are communications with other departments in the company suitable for optimum use of technical information in improving operations and in commercializing new products and processes?

In the following paragraphs these principles will first be discussed in terms of their application to an individual enterprise. Attention will then be turned briefly to the problems of an industrial sector, and finally to a national economy.

Planning Objectives and Criteria

In industrialized economies, managements of enterprises are adopting in increasing number the concept called "corporate planning" or "corporate development," which is discussed more fully in a later chapter. These terms signify the systematic process of defining objectives and of setting criteria to evaluate projects proposed as means for reaching these goals. It is essential that these objectives and criteria be considered as dynamic, that is, subject to modification as deemed necessary because of internal developments in operations or external situations having a bearing on the future program.

If statements of management objectives and criteria are lacking, the technical program may well become diffuse and unproductive through lack of guidance as to plans for modification, extension, or diversification of operations. Because individual research projects are aimed at developments to be commercialized some time in the future, they in particular need to be directed at goals which have been defined by the managers of the enterprise.

This type of general guidance is required so that the program can provide answers to such questions as the following: If different raw materials will be needed to meet the goals, what specifications can be set and what effect will the composition or physical form of new sources of supply have on process and on quality of finished product? What types of new or modified products are contemplated, and what performance characteristics, materials, equipment and processes are needed for their successful commercialization?

Outlining the Technical Program

Once the enterprise goals and criteria have been formulated, the technical manager is in position to plan the type of program needed to produce the information for which he will be responsible. What are the major work areas and what are the relative priorities: raw material evaluation, process adaptation or improvement, product development, or technical service? What project system can be devised in terms of objectives, timing, and balance between short-range and long-range work? How can these requirements be interpreted in terms of staff and facilities needed? What assistance should management give in helping to establish the coordination with other departments of the enterprise needed to define specific objectives more exactly and to implement the results of the technical work?

During the period in which this operating philosophy is being developed by the technical manager, he should maintain contact with company management to make sure that his analysis of the requirements for the program is in harmony with general objectives. Not only may these undergo change because of internal and external developments, but also his evaluation of the technical feasibility of certain proposed steps may lead to modification of the goals and criteria.

Organization and Administration

When the general outlines of the program have been laid out, the technical manager then needs to set up an organization and to establish administrative procedures for the conduct of the work. A system is required for defining technical objectives, setting priorities, estimating personnel and time requirements, assigning personnel and reviewing their performance, instituting procedures for reporting, and establishing relationships with management and operating departments for re-evaluation of progress in terms of practical application.

These administrative procedures can be most effectively carried out by means of a project system, the operation of which will be discussed in more detail in later chapters. This involves breaking the program into appropriate segments, each of which is defined in terms of objective, estimated amount of technical effort required, estimated cost, proposed method of attack, and target date. When taken together, the projects comprise the backbone of the program as a whole. Their sum in terms of technical effort is limited by the amount of technical man-power to be made available, and their priorities must be adjusted within this framework.

Coordination with Other Departments

If the research and development work is to be effective, it must not operate in a vacuum as far as the rest of the company is concerned. First of all, the program must be reviewed periodically with management for assurance that the projects are in harmony with current plans. Then it should be reviewed in a suitable manner with representatives of operating and staff groups, including manufacturing, engineering, marketing, and finance.

Reviews with operating and staff groups serve three purposes: First, they help to sharpen objectives of the research, by affording realistic re-appraisal of available raw materials, process and equipment limitations, and performance specifications for final products. Secondly, they bring about a better psychological climate toward innovation in the entire organization by making other groups feel that they are participating in the projects in an advisory way. Finally, they give advance warning to those who will be concerned with various aspects of stepping up the new product or process to commercial scale, in order that they may have their plans and programs prepared when the research and development phase is completed.

Programs for Sectors of Industry

The problem of guidance of research and development becomes more complex when the program is aimed at serving a sector of industry made up of several separate enterprises under separate managements. The status of technology may vary widely in the different companies. The receptivity toward new ideas and toward innovative processes and products may differ, and there may be built-in obstacles to innovation, such as raw material availability, equipment limitations, and differences in the markets served.

A primary consideration is an analysis of what technical strengths are needed in the individual operations, under their own local control, and what can effectively be provided from a central source. It was emphasized at the beginning of this chapter that technical back-up is a necessity for most manufacturing operations of any size, and this service is best provided by staff who are in intimate contact with the problems. The greater the geographical and administrative separation from the scene of action, the more difficult it is to transmit a full understanding of operating difficulties required for a practical solution, and to give the necessary impetus to implementation. A major function of an industry technical center is therefore to determine those areas in which the component companies are in greatest need of professional assistance, to institute projects for demonstrating the value of such help, and eventually to work with individual units in planning and installing their own functions.

Industry programs call for effective communications with individuals representing a cross-section of the components. This can be obtained through advisory committees with memberships reflecting the range of technical status in the entire group of enterprises. Their major function is to define key problem areas in the industry, and to review project proposals for aiding in their solution. A technical information service is helpful in keeping regular contact with the individual managements.

Occasions should be provided in which the entire program of the central technical organization can be presented and discussed with representatives of all the units involved. When new or improved products or processes are to be introduced, it is best to select a suitable firm for the purpose of introducing the operation on a practical basis; this installation can then be used as a demonstration plant, which serves as an information center for other companies that may be interested. This procedure will usually result in more effective action than would be attained by general presentations to the industry as a whole.

Some type of practical technical assistance to all the units in the industry is very desirable, particularly for the purpose of cementing effective communication. A helpful plan is to develop a system of quality evaluation, in which each unit submits samples of product on a periodic basis; the results are reported back, together with a summary of data from the industry as a whole. There are numerous cases in which this scheme has been used in the food and textile industries, for example, with the end result of raising the general level of quality among the participants. Another useful form of assistance is to conduct a "best practices" survey of the status of technology in all units. A study of this type was carried out, for example, by an ADL team and industrial representatives in the cottonseed oil industry in Egypt several years ago.

It should be noted that all these types of service are aimed at developing direct contacts with all enterprises on a regular basis.

Technical Programming on a National Basis

The underlying philosophy in programs for research and development for individual companies or industries discussed in the preceding sections is to plan the over-all program on the basis of selected individual projects. Through identification of key problems and proposing courses of action to solve them, followed by setting priorities, available technical man-power can be suitably deployed in terms of emphasis to be placed on competing projects.

The prerequisite for technical programming on a country-wide basis is, of course, national planning based on national needs and resources. From this foundation the technical planners can formulate objectives, goals, and criteria for evaluating projects in terms of the national policy and program. The problem is complex, not only because of the breadth of problems covered, but also because technical men are not interchangeable in their areas of competence, but should be used in assignments for which their specialized training and experience qualify them.

The central authority, therefore, needs to encourage individual enterprises and groups of enterprises to carry out objective analyses of their technical status versus requirements. The better they document their specific situations and needs, the more complete will be the total picture of technology in the country. From this analytical base, the central authorities will be in the best position to determine constructively the voids, underemphasis, or overemphasis in component programs as related to national policy. This is an area which calls for joint efforts of technologists and economists.

This philosophy is grounded on the belief that, while over-all plans should be based on general objectives and criteria, the synthesis of the technical program should be made from the composite of individual projects and requirements, to permit logical analysis of priorities and appropriate allocation of technical resources.

CHAPTER **3**   TECHNOLOGIC NEEDS
OF DEVELOPING
ECONOMIES

Resource Utilization in National Perspective

"One of the great questions before any nation concerns the adequacy
of natural resources to provide the kind of living its people want, or in some
countries, merely to keep the population alive. The question is not new or tran-
sient. Even in the United States, with large resources of land, water, energy,
and minerals, and the world's highest average level of living, one finds concern
regarding the over-all adequacy of resources to support the rate of growth of the
economy that is within the nation's reach. And if sheer quantities of raw materials and of resource services will suffice, then what will happen to the quality
of the resource base itself and its capacity to sustain further economic growth?
How may resource conservation and development reflect proven social values
and at the same time promote such changes as society at its best would like to
make? More specifically, can the flow of useful materials be increased without
higher costs? Can necessary imports of raw materials be obtained effectively
in ways that at the same time contribute to the economic development of the
supplying countries? What reliance can be placed on discovery of new sources,
and on technological advances in extraction, processing, and use? Can shifts
in demand from one material to another be foreseen and accomplished with
minimum disturbance to the existing work force and pattern of industrial location?
What are the prospects for surplus production as well as for shortage of particular items? These are some of the questions that gave rise to this book, which
essentially is an effort to build a framework within which answers may be worked
out."

This quotation is from the preface to "Resources in America's Future,"
published in 1963 by The Johns Hopkins Press. The monograph carries the sub-
title "Patterns of Requirements and Availabilities, 1960-2000." The authors are
Landsberg, Fischman, and Fisher, of Resources for the Future, Inc. The section quoted is an excellent statement of the broad problems that are stimulating
analysis of national resources throughout the world.

Many studies of this type have been carried out in developing countries
in recent years, particularly under the U.S. foreign aid program. They involve,
as major phases, the establishment of an objective appraisal of the present status
of the economy with respect to resources of raw materials and existing manufactures according to conventional classifications, an estimate of potential consumptive
capacity in domestic and foreign markets for the different categories of goods
either in original form or in up-graded state, and a comprehensive review of the
means by which the products of the country can be better utilized for the national
welfare. These mechanisms for industrial development include the gamut of
resources for increasing the yield or availability of consumable products through

15

improvements in the technology of assembling them, transporting them to processing or marketing areas, and enhancing their marketability through some form of
processing. Pertinent subjects are: (1) the availability of suitable labor and
specialized competence such as managerial and technical talents and (2) the means
by which capital can be made available for financing needed facilities.

Criteria for Evaluating Projects

In a developing economy, individual projects need to be reviewed from
the point of view of their compatibility with the national interest. The primary
purpose of an industrial enterprise, assuming that it is in harmony with the broad
objectives of the country, is to contribute to the national welfare by developing
itself as a self-sustaining undertaking which generates a positive return to the
economy.

The following are basic points for consideration as justification for a
project: (1) providing gainful employment, thus contributing to the standard of
living; (2) enhancing national self-sufficiency; (3) satisfying needs of consumers
by providing products at economic cost; (4) utilizing natural resources, either
by primary recovery or upgrading; (5) adding to favorable balance of trade in
international commerce; (6) recovering values from wastes or by-products.

Utilization of Natural Resources

Attention is being given increasingly in mature economies to evaluation
of their natural resources, as mentioned in the first section. This type of study
is even more important in developing countries, since their raw materials are
a logical foundation for the creation of new enterprises.

Many developing countries are undertaking the preparation of systematic
catalogs of their raw materials. These include quantitative surveys of available
primary products, evaluation of their quality against commercial standards, and
determination of suitability for processing or up-grading. The scientist and
technologist play leading parts in such surveys.

An important aspect is insurance of optimum utilization. Losses of
perishable materials, such as agricultural produce, reach deplorable levels
through mechanical wastage, spoilage, and damage by pests. This is a field offering great opportunities for decentralized preliminary processing for preserva-
tion until the products reach the final manufacturing operation or the consumer.
The problems are peculiar to each region and the solutions require original
thinking and new product and process development. A somewhat related topic is
reduction in use of critical materials, particularly those imported, in fabrication
or construction through elimination of over-design.

Initial Steps for Using Technical Resources

In mature economies much attention is being devoted to the question of how smaller companies without their own research and development can acquire the new and improved technology they need. Government agencies and trade associations are particularly active in this respect. Obviously there is a great deal of technical information available for these purposes, but the problem is to bring it into focus and adapt it to a particular situation.

There are two essential steps which can be classed under the broad heading of technical communication: The first is for the company to select an individual, preferably with some scientific or engineering background, to undertake the responsibility of serving as a technical focus, on a part-time basis if necessary. He should be receptive to new ideas and interested in trying to adopt them practically. The second step is to seek out his counterpart in the world of science and technology, either a group or an individual willing to devote time to learning something of the practical side of the particular operation, to sift the resources of technical information to find what solutions may be available, and to cooperate in adapting them to the given case.

The problem of supplying technical information to industry in developing economies bears considerable resemblance to that encountered in industrialized countries in efforts to improve the technology of smaller companies. This subject has been receiving much attention since World War II. In both cases, there is need to rely on outside sources. In the United States, the Small Business Administration has been the agency most concerned. Several years ago, it sponsored a project at Arthur D. Little, Inc., headed by A. A. Smith, to prepare a summary of sources of information. The study resulted in a booklet entitled "Technology and Your New Products," published by the U.S. Government Printing Office. The scope is best illustrated by listing the contents. Preparation of a similar brochure would be advantageous in developing economies to describe the technical resources available locally.

The purpose of a brochure of this type is to inform industry of the sources of information suited to its needs. The purpose of any program for encouraging new technology, however, is the other side of the coin, namely, how the sources of technical help can orient themselves to assist industrial enterprises and the national economy.

Outline of "Technology and Your New Products"

I. About Technology

   1. Why Technology?

     Distinction between science and technology; What large industry has done; What small industry can do; Case histories.

   2. Some Definitions

     Quality control techniques; Technical service; Product and Process development; Research; How technology grows within a company.

   3. Some Implications

     Questions to ask; Factors to estimate; Thinking it through; Policy to consider.

   4. Technology, Small Business, and New Products; Small business and its use of research; Technology rather than pure research.

II. About New Products

   1. Where Do Ideas Come From?

     Importance of assigning responsibility; Kind of personnel needed; Ideas from research; Imagination; Existing developments; Recognizing unfilled needs.

   2. How Good are They?

     Evaluation of new product ideas; Mortality of new ideas; Criteria for evaluation; Market evaluation.

   3. How Do You Produce New Products?

     New product development personnel; Procedures to follow; Equipment requirement; Use of trade literature.

   4. How Do You Sell New Products?

     Product testing for market success; Ways of conducting market research; Role of the small business manager.

III. About Outside Help

    1. Keeping up With the Field

       Importance of keeping up-to-date; Exchanging information;
       Usefulness of professional meetings.

    2. Free Advice

       Using trade and technical publications; Available government
       material; Technical service from larger firms.

    3. Technical Help From Outside

       Why consulting services; Case histories; Different kinds of
       consulting.

    4. Further Information and Guidance

       Importance of reading; Exhibits and conventions; Universities,
       Government laboratories, and technical societies.

Introductory Stages of Technical Programs

A parallel for developing countries may be drawn from the historical
evolution of research and development in companies in industrialized nations.
Usually the first step has been the establishment of a quality control laboratory
with a one-man staff. The individual is at first engaged in routine analysis for
maintaining acceptability of product and policing quality of purchased raw materials. When operating troubles develop in the plant or in servicing customers,
sooner or later he is called on for help on technical service problems. Then,
competitive technology in the industry and the resultant need for new products
confronts the company, and he has to hire an assistant to keep up with his work
load. Finally, the research and development activity becomes important enough
to be set up separately.

The moral is that technical innovation in many companies starts
through quality control. This evolution is happening even today in the United
States, particularly in smaller companies in older industries. Requirements
of the market place (for example, Government specifications for purchase of
textile products in World War II) make it necessary to begin the use of science.

It is suggested, therefore, that one fertile field in developing countries lies in finding means for helping individual enterprises in their quality control. This will not only serve as an entering wedge for science, but will improve conservation of raw materials and efficiency of operations.

Quality control has been looked down upon in the past by many highly trained scientists as uninspiring drudgery. Actually it is one of the best routes, if imaginatively approached, for becoming familiar with the technology of an enterprise and for identifying research and development projects. More and more effort is being devoted in research laboratories to devise new quality control methodology. As a consoling philosophy for those motivated toward pure science, let us remember that much scientific progress comes from finding better ways to measure what is taking place in the world around us, and quality control in industry is one aspect of this approach.

Utilizing Wastes and By-Products

The general idea of converting wastes and by-products into useful materials is very appealing. Successful projects have the glamor of creating something out of nothing. When soundly conceived and executed, they can contribute importantly to the enterprise and to the economy as a whole, as, for example, the part played by furfural from corn cobs in the early development of the nylon industry.

Great caution needs to be exercised in selecting by-product utilization projects to make sure that the potential benefits are proportionate to the work involved. Unfortunately there are many pit-falls, and research department files are full of reports of wasted effort. These usually do not get publicized, because unsuccessful projects are not news-worthy unless they are catastrophic.

Any proposed major project of this type should be carefully evaluated from the point of view of technical economics. A common failure is to regard the waste or by-product as having zero value when it is charged into process costs. Accepted accounting practice dictates, however, that such materials, when used in other operations, should bear their proper allocation of direct costs and indirect overheads, with the result that on final analysis the economic balance of an assumed new use may be unfavorable. Another major difficulty is failure to evaluate objectively on a long-term basis the volume and accessibility of waste that will be available; improvements or changes in the primary operation may markedly alter the quantity, composition, or form of the waste materials.

Obtaining New Technology from Abroad

No stigma of technical inadequacy should be attached to a policy of obtaining information or know-how from external sources. Companies in highly industrialized countries are continually doing this, as a means of gaining time in installing new processes or new products, and as a means of conserving technical resources rather than needlessly duplicating developments that have already been made elsewhere. This may be done through purchase or license of patents, information, or know-how, or of buying turn-key plants. Another route is through pooling resources by joint venture, acquisition, or merger with a company already established in an industrial field which the company wishes to enter.

Obtaining information from external sources is of even greater importance in a developing economy in order that it may speed up industrial development and at the same time conserve its technical resources. It must be recognized that considerable technical back-up will be required for the operation locally, even for a turn-key plant.

Many of the processes and items of equipment purchased abroad will be highly automated as a result of the trend toward conservation of labor. Hence they may not be ideally suited to the general aim of developing economies to raise the living standards by creating a maximum number of jobs in industry. On the other hand, the high degree of automation contributes to better control of operation. Eventually, too, the manufacturing process should be of optimum efficiency to compete with foreign plants, because of the trend toward international competition.

Assessment of Resources of Technical Manpower

Emphasizing again the belief that the greatest source of technical strength in a country is its population of trained personnel, it should be obvious that the starting point for economic development should be comprehensive knowledge of the size, quality, and deployment of this collection of talents. Unfortunately, this point seems to receive insufficient attention, although the mechanisms for obtaining the information have been available.

The facts needed can be obtained by a nation-wide survey of professional personnel engaged in scientific and engineering pursuits, including those in Government departments, industry, and institutions for education and research. A completely pre-coded questionnaire was developed in 1941 for the American Chemical Society by L. W. Bass and Andrew Fraser, Jr., to obtain information on educational background, years of professional experience, field of employment, type of employment, technical area of specialization, geographical location, and occupational status in a form suitable for statistical

analysis. Similar questionnaires have since been used by other technical groups
in the United States, and in recent years the National Science Foundation has
adapted it for compiling data on all professional personnel in the nation. As yet,
there does not appear to be information of comparable detail in other countries.

In a developing nation, such data are imperative for establishing
policies to encourage strategic use of technical manpower. What plans should
be developed for more logical distribution of trained personnel among educational
institutions, government agencies, and industrial operations? Are the strengths
in various sectors of technology and science in balance with the judgments as to
relative needs? What projections can be made for future requirements of
scientists and engineers and in what categories? Central planning for a large-
scale technical effort is difficult at best, and certainly can be done more effectively when good data are available on the existing pattern.

Census of Technical Activities

In addition to knowledge concerning the deployment of trained personnel,
information about individual technical programs is a valuable asset for framing
national policies. It is often assumed that such data have been collected, when
in fact they are incomplete.

In the United States, the National Research Council has been collecting information from industrial companies on a voluntary basis since 1920. The
data include size of research and development departments and major technical
areas. The listings are revised every few years and the published summary is
now in its eleventh edition. This publication is valuable as a list of contacts for
specialized information and as a birdseye view of research activities in different
organizations and industries. Other compilations of Government and university
activities are available.

Surveys of all technical programs are desirable in developing countries
as a means for bringing about better coordination of the total scientific and
engineering effort. The data should include size and qualifications of staff,
major areas of competence, and special facilities such as research equipment
and libraries. The coverage should include Government departments, industrial
firms, research institutes, and educational institutions. Without such information, any attempts to develop a national philosophy for scientific and industrial
development are handicapped.

Several precautions should be observed to obtain good responses to
questionnaires, because many managers feel they are being overwhelmed with
inquiries, the details of which do not seem to be useful. First of all, the value
of the information to the respondent, as well as to the body making the survey,
should be clearly expressed. A commitment to return a summary of the data
to those participating will often encourage participation. The questionnaire
should be framed in such a way--pre-coding is advantageous--that it is easy to
answer and easy to tabulate. Questions which do not serve a useful purpose
should be avoided.

For example, industrial enterprises should be willing to cooperate
actively in a survey of research and development, because the information will
be valuable to them in assessing their technical programs in comparison with
other companies in their industries and with the norms in other countries where
available. Such matters as average total cost of a technical man-year and
break-down of research expense into major categories should be of assistance in
analyzing their own experience. Data of these types are obviously useful to
planning agencies at the national level.

CHAPTER **4**   CHARACTERIZATION AND
RELATIONSHIPS OF
TECHNICAL FUNCTIONS

Definitions of Technical Functions

In the following paragraphs are given definitions of different types of technical work. These are in general accord with current usage in America and Western Europe. They are used in this monograph as a means of emphasizing differences in the degree to which experimentation can be planned in advance, and to reflect increasing scale of work and intensity of economic analysis.

There is some difference of opinion about the ultimate usefulness and significance of such definitions. There are certainly no sharp divisions between the functions. Some writers go so far as to say that a particular investigation could be classed as fundamental research if the scientist had as his objective the discovery of new knowledge, whereas it should be considered applied research if he had in mind a specific practical use for the information, even though the course and quality of the investigation were identical in the two cases.

In spite of the confusion and disagreement in applying the definitions to a particular instance, they have utility as labels for the kinds of work and degrees of innovation involved at different stages in the evolution of a commercial product or process from the original concept. They assist in maintaining balance in a program. They help to define the types of technical talents which are needed.

The activities in these various categories are later discussed in detail in a series of chapters.

Fundamental Research denotes the search for new knowledge without regard to practical utility. It is the historic type of investigation, often called "pure research," carried out in universities and institutions for the purpose of satisfying scientific curiosity and developing theories to explain natural phenomena. It is the classical procedure for training advanced students in the methodology of scientific inquiry and analysis. It is often the source of new technologic break-throughs, but these are usually uncovered by other scientists who are oriented toward practical problems.

Basic Research, more aptly called "oriented long-range research" in many industrial laboratories, denotes the use of scientific methodology in selected fields of present or potential practical interest to the company, but the work is not concerned with immediate commercial objectives. It is conducted not only for the results it may itself yield, but also to maintain effective contact with the world of science, from which pertinent information from outside sources may be focused on the barrier problems of the enterprise or industry. Basic research projects are normally of long-range character, and five years or more of sustained effort may be required before they result in direct commercial application. There may be valuable by-products from such projects, however, because interim findings may have utility in solving current applied problems.

In highly developed economies, usually only the largest companies in science-based industries support basic research. In such enterprises, its magnitude may amount to 10 percent or more of the research and development budget. It poses problems for successful administration, which will be discussed in a later section.

Applied Research, often termed "product-directed" or "process-directed research," is concerned with the evaluation of existing knowledge, originally obtained from fundamental research (which may or may not have been carried out within the particular organization), for adaptability to commercial products or processes, or to innovative developments. Projects of this type usually require two to five years before their results are commercialized.

Product and Process Development is the term frequently employed to designate work of small or intermediate scale undertaken to apply new technology and materials to defined objectives for products and processes. It is the type of activity involved in shorter-range projects for expansion of existing product lines or for improvement of existing processes. It is also a stage in implementing the findings from longer-range applied researches, after these have progressed to the point at which specific end-uses can be visualized. Target dates are usually set at several months to two years ahead for the completion of this phase.

The term "development" is also often used to denote pre-pilot- or pilot-scale work to demonstrate the technical feasibility of laboratory findings on equipment approaching commercial plant in philosophy of design and operation. Such work provides data required for design of full-scale plant and confirms engineering and economic analysis.

Technical Service to Manufacturing is the use of technical information and know-how to assist the commercial plant in solving operating problems. It may be carried out by technologists or engineers on the staff of the manufacturing department or, if it requires specialized knowledge or more work than they are prepared to undertake, it may be referred to the research and development department. The problems are of relatively short-range character, but if they cannot be solved readily, they may be made the subjects of research projects for more intensive investigation.

Technical Service to Marketing is the use of technical information and know-how to assist customers in using the company's products. In many organizations this activity is established within the marketing department itself.

Quality Control Methodology denotes the critical examination of laboratory control methods and procedures to effect improvements in accuracy, economy, utility, and significance of tests in maintaining or improving quality.

Quality Control is concerned with the systematic use of established laboratory and inspection methods and procedures to ensure that raw materials, intermediates, and finished products meet required specifications. Quality control results may be incorporated in programs directed toward the analysis of efficiency of production operations.

Relationships Among Technical Functions

The manner in which the previously defined functions coalesce in the evolution of a new commercial product or process is presented in Figure 1, called "The Technologic Pyramid." This geometrical form reflects roughly the order of magnitude of technical effort that may be involved at successive stages.

Science in the World Reservoir calls attention to the vast store of knowledge in the scientific literature and in the minds of other scientists, which is available to all who take steps to seek it. The research director of a large American company, which maintains a world-famous basic research laboratory, has stated that their budget permits them to carry out less than one percent of the total fundamental research they feel to be necessary for adequate technologic advances in their industry.

Scientific Intelligence, usually performed by scientists in the basic research sector of a company, involves screening world science for information or ideas that may apply to the company's projects.

Basic Research consists of projects aimed at supplying data and theories in scientific areas of interest to the enterprise. The research carried out is often made available through publication. The scientists engaged in such work, because they must follow the literature in their respective fields and have contact with their fellows from external laboratories, are an important factor in scientific intelligence.

Technologic Feasibility Studies are helpful as a first step to determine whether new scientific knowledge appears to have potential value for practical application.

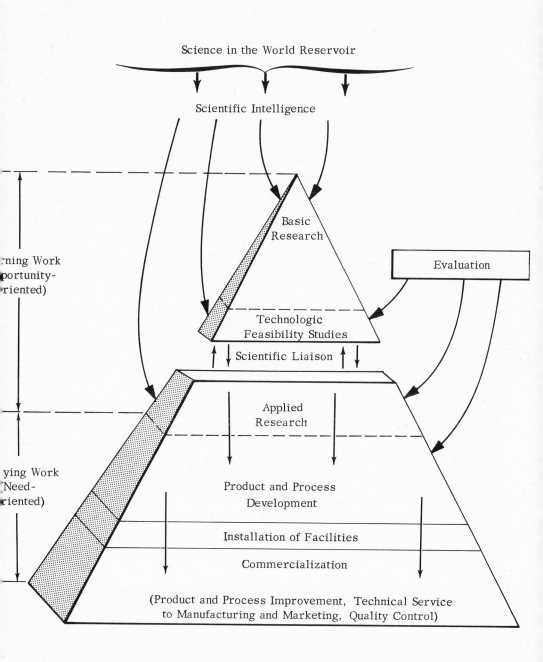

Science in the World Reservoir

Scientific Intelligence

Basic Research

Evaluation

ning Work
portunity-
riented)

Technologic Feasibility Studies

Scientific Liaison

Applied Research

ying Work
Need-
ciented)

Product and Process Development

Installation of Facilities

Commercialization

(Product and Process Improvement, Technical Service to Manufacturing and Marketing, Quality Control)

FIGURE 1   THE TECHNOLOGIC PYRAMID

27

Scientific Liaison between Basic Research and Applied Research is often felt to be desirable in large organizations. The function can be carried out by a small group of competent scientists who are gifted in recognizing new knowledge that may have practical significance. They may concurrently be devoting part of their time to their own researches. Their value is in calling the attention of applied scientists to interesting new basic knowledge, either from within the company or elsewhere in the world, and also in carrying back to the basic science group information about needs for new knowledge to aid technologic advances.

Applied Research is a more detailed study to define the commercial potential of technical information in terms of suitability of raw materials and processes and of utility of products in terms of customer needs.

Product and Process Development is the larger-scale work required to confirm the findings of Applied Research. It involves to an increasing degree analysis of economic factors, namely, the estimated cost of producing the product and the selling price which would be attractive to potential users.

Technical Activities Required by Production are those types of work that are needed to maintain efficiency of manufacturing and utility of product. These are classified as Quality Control, Technical Service to Manufacturing and Marketing, and Product and Process Improvement.

CHAPTER **5** CORPORATE
LOGISTICS AND
PRODUCT POLICY

The Life Cycle of Technology

It has been pointed out that rapid advances in technology have conditioned industrial managers in highly developed countries to the expectation that their products and processes will sooner or later undergo obsolescence. It is common to find statements in corporate reports that large fractions of total sales and profits are currently being derived from products introduced in a short span of years.

A typical first stage in the life history of an innovative new product is a rapid acceleration in volume with a high degree of profitability because it is filling a market need in a new way. This is the justification for undertaking the development and market introduction, because hopefully the cost of pioneering will be paid off through larger profits. This happy situation naturally attracts competition - direct and indirect - and after a time lag other companies find ways to enter the same product or service area. Volume may still increase, but initial profitability will gradually drop. Next, the product, together with its competitors, will reach a plateau. Finally, it will begin to wane in volume and profitability as more recent innovations crowd it out.

A company's total business is based on a range of products in various stages of youthful vigor, hearty middle age, and decaying senescence. The future of the enterprise depends on managerial skill in guiding corporate development so that the product mix consists of a backlog of firmly entrenched lines and a rejuvenating flow of innovations. This logistic approach requires the development of corporate objectives to define the planned directions of growth. But in turn this commercial development program hinges on the new technology which is generated internally or acquired from outside.

Characterization of "New Products"

The magic symbol of successful corporate development is new products. But these differ greatly in their impact on the business, depending on their character. They may be merely minor modifications of existing products which are limited in effect to modest increases in sales to regular customers at the normal rate of profit for the established product line. At the other end of the spectrum, they may represent diversification into new marketing areas with very attractive profit margins. An objective appraisal of the significance of the various categories is essential for sound managerial philosophy.

The confusion as to business aspects of different kinds of "new products" carries over to the analysis of research programs. Some individuals may
have in mind when they speak of a "new product" anything that is not presently
being marketed by the company, even though it is very closely related to present
products in composition, form, raw materials, manufacturing process, manner
of use by customers, marketing and distribution system, and profitability. The
course of development and evaluation in this case will usually be relatively short
and inexpensive. Others may be thinking in terms of a product that is innovative
in concept and performance and meets the needs of customers in a different way;
here development and evaluation may be very time-consuming and costly.

In order that new product programs may be more intelligently managed, there must be better understanding of the characteristics of the product
ideas under consideration. New definitions for this purpose have recently been
formulated by the author, and in the rest of this monograph the terminology will
be as follows:

1. New items are products closely related to the present
    line which can be marketed with little change in mar-
    keting channels, service, or strategy.

2. New products are innovative in character and enable
    the company to offer materials to satisfy customers'
    needs in a more effective way but still are within the
    marketing areas already being served; they require
    more extensive service to show the consumer how
    they can best be used.

3. New product lines are new businesses which lead the
    company into entirely new marketing areas and re-
    quire a different distribution strategy and organization.

The benefits and risks to be considered in undertaking projects of
these three types are summarized in Table 3.

One can foresee many internal arguments about the proper classification of a product under consideration unless some ground rules are set. To this
end a list of 14 criteria, most of which refer to marketing aspects, is given in
Table 4. Four of the criteria are not determinative; five show transition from
new items to new products; and five from new products to new product lines.
There will, of course, be numerous cases in which one or more criteria do not
fit this idea model, but at least this type of analysis will facilitate realistic
classification.

TABLE 3

BENEFITS AND RISKS OF NEW ITEMS, NEW PRODUCTS,
AND NEW PRODUCT LINES

	New Items	New Products	New Product Lines
Relationship to present products	Close	Innovative	Radically different
Risk	Moderate	Considerable	Large
Development cost	Moderate	Considerable	Large
Market analysis	Moderate	Important	Demanding
Cost of market intro-duction	Moderate	Important	Large
Technical service	Minor	Important	Large
Investment	Routine	Important	Large
Profitability	Routine	Improved	Attractive
Impact on the enterprise	Re-enforce present position	Enhance market penetration	Major diversi-fication

The purpose of these distinctions is to clarify the character of any project in terms of the hazards and advantages to the enterprise. In later sections this discussion will be extended to the implications of balance between short-term and long-term projects in the total research program.

TABLE 4

CRITERIA FOR CLASSIFICATION OF ADDED PRODUCTS

	Present Product Line	New Items	New Products	New Product Lines
Non-Determinative Criteria				
Composition and/or Physical Characteristics		Differences throughout		
Raw Materials		May be the same or different		
Process		" " " " " "		
Packaging		" " " " " "		
Differentiation Between New Items and New Products				
Quality Standards	———	Change	Change	
Pattern of Uses	———	Change	Change	
Market Development	———	Change	Change	
Customer Contacts	———	Change	Change	
Technical Service to Customers	———	Change	Change	
Differentiation Between New Products and New Product Lines				
Customer Acceptance of Enterprise Capability (Franchise)	———	———		Change
Trade Channels (Wholesalers, Jobbers, etc.)	———	———		Change
Distribution Staff	———	———		Change
Promotion and Advertising	———	———		Change
Character of Physical Distribution	———	———		Change

Formulation of Product Policy

In order that a product development program may be fruitful, obviously it should be concentrated on products of a type that the company will wish to commercialize if they pass the screening tests of market demand and economic and technologic feasibility.

There are a great many examples, however, some even in companies that are reputed to be well managed, in which heavy effort and expense have improperly been devoted to projects allowed to proceed to pilot production and market development, only to be abandoned because management finally reaches the decision that it does not wish to undertake commercialization. Such decisions, of course, are often based on unforeseen situations which have developed during the interim within the company, within the industry, within the market, or within the general economy. All too often, though, these unfortunate occurrences result from a failure of management to set policies regarding the types of products they are prepared to activate, or a failure of the technical groups to ask for guidance on product areas at earlier stages.

Abandoned developments represent wasted efforts that might have been channeled in more productive directions. The psychological effect, which may be even more serious than the lost time, is the blow to the morale of the groups who were directly involved in the unsuccessful project and logically ask why the decisions were not reached in earlier stages.

To minimize the number of abandoned developments, well-managed companies are turning to written product policies and criteria to serve as guidelines to the various departments concerned with new products. To maintain validity, these policies and criteria should be reviewed and up-dated periodically, at least at annual intervals.

The policies deal with such questions as the following:

Market area: Does the management wish to confine efforts
to present types of customers and end uses? Does it aspire to expand into new areas, and if so what types?
Are there business segments which would appear to be
logical but which the management prefers not to enter?

Types of products: Does the enterprise wish to confine
its efforts to new items, as defined above? Is it prepared
to back ideas for innovative new products for its present
line? Does it desire to enter new market areas with new
product lines, and if the answer is yes, what criteria does
it set? What relative emphasis should be placed on new
items, new products, and new product lines?

Size of undertaking: How large a manufacturing and marketing proposal is the management willing to undertake? Will
it consider a new plant site? Will it be prepared to install
new types of equipment and processing, and if so, within
what limits?

Raw materials: What limitation does the management place
on types of raw materials it will use? If new raw materials
sources need to be developed, how far afield will consideration be extended? If the alternative sources require capital
to develop them, will the management consider such support? What restrictions are placed on imports?

These questions are searching, and adequate answers will not be
forthcoming easily. Hence responsibility for developing product policy should
be delegated to an individual, who should carry out his task by consultation with
his associates in appropriate departments of the company before submitting his
final proposals to management for comment, revision, and approval.

In medium-sized organizations with a Director of Corporate Development, whose functions will be discussed in more detail in a later chapter, this
responsibility is often assigned to him as one of his duties. In larger organizations, where he has a diversified staff, he may appoint a Manager of New Product Development.

Assessment of Corporate Resources for Undertaking New Products

An objective analysis of the strengths and weaknesses of a company is
a prerequisite for a sound product policy. Such a study, often considered the
responsibility of the Director of Corporate Development on behalf of the chief
executive, reveals its capabilities and liabilities for growth. The scope of a
survey of this type includes the following subjects. In diversified companies
each major division or product area should be analyzed separately.

Management - capabilities of top and middle management
for carrying out present responsibilities and undertaking
new ones; depth and degree of utilization of management
resources; factors restricting freedom of action, such
as organizational defects.

Marketing - economic characteristics of product and trade
areas served; capability of marketing staff to handle additional areas; special marketing advantages or handicaps;
customer relations and franchise.

Technology - strength and diversity of professional personnel; areas of technical expertise; working relations with the rest of the company; facilities.

Manufacturing - condition and flexibility of plants, equipment, and process; areas of specialized know-how.

Raw Materials - advantages or handicaps in sources of raw materials, including both those controlled by the company and those purchased from outside.

Growth Potential - future prospects of major product lines; comparison with competitors; outlook for related trade areas which might be considered.

Financial Resources - size and type of financial potential for maintaining present position and for expansion.

If a survey of this type is to be valid for planning purposes, it should be conducted with maximum objectivity and in considerable depth. The individuals selected to carry it out should be mature, experienced, analytical, free from prejudice, and exempt from criticism for frank opinions. Companies often find it difficult to staff a corporate assessment team within the organization; the individuals who might be considered often cannot be spared from other current responsibilities. It has become quite common practice for companies to engage outside consultants to make the studies because of greater objectivity and freedom from organizational pressures.

Responsibilities of New Product Planning

Planning for new products should be entrusted to a mature individual with proven experience in activities essential for developing and executing successful programs of this type. He should have had direct experience in some phase of marketing. He should have an understanding of, and the ability to make use of, such technical activities as market and consumer research, and laboratory research and development.

The Manager, New Product Development, in a large company often reports to the Director of Corporate Development. He must organize, staff, and provide continuing direction for the range of new product activities, comprising market and consumer research, market planning, and coordination with the laboratory program and technical service. He plans and conducts a program for obtaining new product ideas inside and outside the company. He establishes

and reviews new product criteria. These criteria should reflect the findings
from the assessment of corporate resources described in the preceding section.
He directs a program of evaluation of new product ideas by means of these criteria. He undertakes preliminary assessment of initially screened product
ideas for their economic, technical, production, and marketing feasibility, using
help from other groups as needed. He prepares and coordinates the execution of
a program of development for selected products. He is responsible for programs
of consumer and market research on new products under development. He ar-
ranges for detailed economic analysis of feasibility of new products.

Management of Product Suggestion Systems

Worthwhile suggestions for new items, new products, or new product
lines can come from a wide variety of sources:

1. Suggestions from technical departments;

2. Suggestions from the marketing organization;

3. Suggestions from the manufacturing staff;

4. Management suggestions;

5. Product planning working groups;

6. Customer or trade wants or desires as relayed back
    from the market place by salesmen, agents, and dis-
    tributors;

7. Customer complaints on existing products indicating
    areas for improvement;

8. Continuing analysis of customer needs and behaviors
    through market research;

9. Advertising agencies;

10. Pressures from rising cost of materials or manufac-
    turing operations;

11. Competitive pressure when selling prices of competi-
    tors' products, including imports, are lower;

12. Consultants;

13. Trade and technical literature;

14. Patents - active or expired;

15. Government publications or services;

16. Sponsored research projects.

The relative importance of the various sources of product ideas will show wide differences in different organizations, but the historical experience of an individual company should be a good guide regarding the sources that should be stimulated. An American survey several years ago of over 100 laboratories gave the following results for major sources of project ideas:

Research	45%
Manufacturing	16%
Marketing	16%
Management	11%
Others	12%

It is good practice for a company to set up an organized system for encouraging a continuing flow of product ideas, evaluating them by orderly procedures, and disposing of them in positive fashion. Frequently an award system is used, which may involve only the prestige of an official citation, but often includes some more tangible form of recognition such as a suitable prize. For a suggestion system to remain constructive in effect, it must be maintained in active operation, and all suggestions should receive definite disposition, either by adoption, starting a development project, or rejection, and the originators should be notified of the decision in each case. Otherwise, the motivation to submit ideas deteriorates, and the number of suggestions declines.

If a company management decides to establish a policy and program for encouraging product ideas, it should do so on a practical basis which it feels sure it can continue. It is better to make a beginning on a modest scale, which can then be increased as experience dictates. If the start is so elaborate that it cannot be maintained, there is likely to be a great burst of enthusiasm which dies out in a few months as the impetus is lost because of inability to carry out constructive handling of the suggestions.

CHAPTER **6**   ELEMENTS OF
TECHNICAL
PROGRAMMING

Scope of Managerial Responsibilities

As orientation for the discussion of different technical functions in subsequent chapters, this introduction is concerned with placing them in the perspective of the program as a whole. The purpose is to suggest guidelines for determining the range, character, and size of the projects that can be undertaken, the framework within which their priorities can be set, and the professional climate that needs to be created.

Establishment of management objectives for growth of the company sets the stage for technical programming. The goals for new products need to be evaluated in terms of scientific and engineering feasibility as well as from the standpoint of business economics. Hence the feedback from the research and development department is a necessary input in testing the validity of the proposed development projects. The commitment of technical effort for each undertaking has to be weighed against its potential value to the company and has to be compared with the attractiveness of alternative lines of work, including those already underway. Final judgment eventually rests with top management, but documented analysis of technical considerations is a prerequisite for sound decision making.

Directors of research and development are exposed to the temptation of becoming immersed in technical aspects to such an extent that they may take managerial functions for granted. They may lose sight of the importance of administrative policies and procedures required to ensure productive use of the scientific and engineering talents of the staff. They may fail to devote the necessary attention to techniques for planning, assigning responsibility, supervising, evaluating performance, and coordinating relationships required for implementing results, all of which are involved in successful leadership of professional personnel. Above all, they may overlook the problems inherent in keeping work flowing in selected channels without inhibiting the creative ability of the staff.

Analysis of Program and Technical Resources

Review should be carried out on a continuing basis of the deployment of personnel versus the merits of individual lines of work. Managerial inertia leads to a pattern of commitments to historic activities without questioning the justification for magnitude and type of effort. Resources for increasing other projects or undertaking new ones are thus curtailed.

A general concept which is useful in analyzing the content of a program is the distinction between defensive and aggressive work. This classification demonstrates to management the inherent necessity for much technical activity - usually at least half of the budget and frequently much more - just to maintain a competitive position. This is a priority requirement which must be met. Work aimed at innovative products and processes, therefore, has to be accommodated from the remainder of available manpower.

Defensive activities include the development of new items for the product line (using the definition of the previous chapter), product and process improvement, technical service to manufacturing and marketing, and work connected with the quality control program. They tend to fall into a fixed pattern that is not subjected to critical questioning. They are usually undertaken at the request of operating departments, which may impose an unduly heavy load on research and development rather than develop the necessary technical strengths internally to handle service work. Because the individual undertakings are characteristically not large, it is a temptation to accept them without careful analysis of their justification in terms of effort versus potential benefits. By collecting these defensive activities into the larger classifications mentioned above, the size of their burden emerges and managerial scrutiny becomes meaningful.

Aggressive activities include work on new products and new product lines, the development of new processes including scaling up of methods for manufacture of new products, the evaluation and adaptation of important new raw materials, and the exploration of major areas of new uses for existing products. The individual undertakings tend to represent large commitments of technical effort. And because they hold the promise of innovation, they attract more managerial attention than the relatively inconspicuous defensive work. But aggressive projects also can fall into ruts of complacency from which they can be shaken only by vigorous administrative review.

The balance between defensive and aggressive activities is therefore a matter of management policy. If the company is content to maintain a steady position in its industry, in spite of the long range hazard of such an attitude, it will concentrate on defensive projects. If it aspires to dynamic growth, it should find means of emphasizing aggressive technical work.

Project Systems as a Control Procedure

The break-down of a technical program into major classifications of defensive and aggressive work is a first step toward analysis of the disposition of effort. This scheme, however, brings to light only gross characterization.

Experience in highly industrialized countries confirms the benefits of organization of a program into specific projects aimed at defined goals, with provision of a reasonable proportion of unallocated time for exploratory work. Detailed description of the operation of a project system is given in a later chapter, but it is pertinent to describe the principles at this point.

Each major line of work is defined concisely in terms of objective, scope, estimated value to the company, proposed method of attack, manpower requirements, estimated cost of the technical effort, and target date to reach the objective. Project control is most effective if it is based on separate phases involved in carrying an idea from original concept to commercialization. Responsibility for directing each project is assigned to an individual who is accountable for supervising the program and controlling work input by members of the project team as well as budgetary and schedule performance. The staff expenditure of time and associated costs are accumulated and compared with the estimates. The project is reviewed periodically from the point of view of technical and economic feasibility, and interim decisions are reached as to continuation, expansion, contraction, or abandonment.

In addition to major research projects, certain continuing activities (such as technical service to manufacturing and marketing, raw material procurement, or improvement of quality control methods) are set up as service projects, with estimates of manpower requirements and cost for the budgeted period, preferably one year. Time expenditure of personnel and expense for each are accumulated and compared with estimates. It is preferable to maintain a running summary of the individual tasks performed on each continuing project by means of a simple listing system.

The proposed project assignments, including both major investigations and continuing projects, usually account for 80-90 percent of technical manpower, including planned additions to the staff, available during the period of forecast. Leeway is provided for exploratory activities, which are left to the discretion of the laboratory director, usually 10-20 percent of the program. As soon as a subject in the exploratory work reaches a stage at which it is feasible to estimate value and scope of the subject, it is written up in the form of a project proposal for administrative review and authorization.

Mortality of Research Ideas

Suggestions and activated projects for product and process development suffer a high rate of mortality. Many are rejected at a very early stage. Others are abandoned during the course of the work as the results fail to justify continuation.

The following average history of 20 large chemical companies in the United States is reported by H. M Corley in "Successful Commercial Chemical Development" (1954). It traces the fate of a typical original list of 540 ideas evaluated at the research department level:

92 were rejected in the initial screening procedure;
448 were eliminated in conferences to consider new
   product suggestions;
92 were selected for preliminary laboratory study;
8 were sufficiently promising to warrant development
   projects;
7 were dropped at the semi-works stage;
1 survived as a commercial product.

Evaluation and Abandonment of Projects

Experience shows that it is much easier to start a project than it is to stop it. A major advantage of a project system is the fact that it puts a limit on exploratory work by an enthusiastic researcher through the requirement that the subject be reviewed after modest expenditure of effort in order to determine whether the results justify authorization of a project. Further, an approved project should be limited to a phase of the investigation, with the result that critical review is made before the next phases are undertaken.

Efficiency of operation in terms of manpower utilization is promoted by a policy of experimentation on the smallest scale that is feasible for obtaining meaningful results. For example, a project advancing from the research stage to product development will entail a much greater commitment of personnel, and therefore the next phase should be undertaken only after analysis has provided justification. Figure 2 represents the growing demands on manpower resources as the scale of work increases.

Specialized Functions of Other Departments

Only very large laboratories are likely to operate as self-sufficient organizations. In most companies valuable help can be obtained from other departments of the company, which cuts down the number of staff tied up in marginal activities. Such functions as accounting, purchasing, and major problems of maintenance and construction are obvious examples of services that can be provided in this way.

In technical areas a careful appraisal of advantages and disadvantages should be made before decision is reached to establish functions that could be

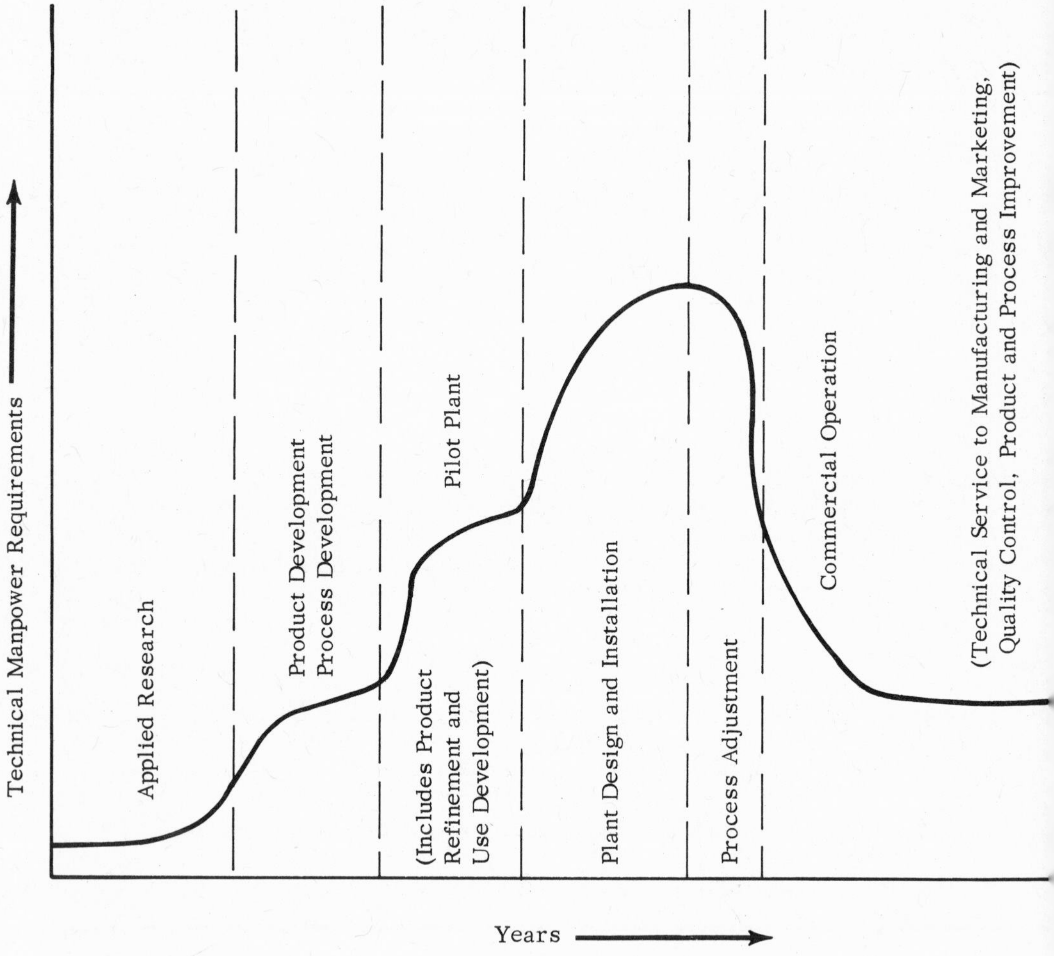

Technical Manpower Requirements →

Years →

Applied Research

Product Development
Process Development

Pilot Plant

(Includes Product
Refinement and
Use Development)

Plant Design and Installation

Process Adjustment

Commercial Operation

(Technical Service to Manufacturing and Marketing,
Quality Control, Product and Process Improvement)

FIGURE 2   TECHNICAL MANPOWER INVOLVED IN A TYPICAL PROJECT

42

supplied by other departments. For example, process engineering, market intelligence, techno-economic analysis, and engineering design and construction may be available on a satisfactory basis, which eliminates the need for including them in the scope of the technical department. Arrangements have to be established by the research executive regarding priorities and speed of service, control of depth of study, and channels of communication to assure himself that his requirement can be taken care of effectively. By these means he can avoid setting up special groups which sequester manpower from the mainstream of research and development, and also can minimize the tendency for such groups to expand to handle peak loads, and thus to become overstaffed for normal requirements.

Analysis of Total Program

From the above discussion we conclude that competent technical management requires mechanisms for systematic review of all segments of program from the points of view of technical feasibility, economic justification, and consonance with management objectives. Decisions must be reached, within the framework of relative merits of alternative use of technical resources, to continue an investigation, expand or decrease the scale, or to abandon or postpone further work.

Reviews are facilitated by a project system which provides a measure of manpower required versus value of objective, and a firmer basis for evaluation in terms of corporate goals. The composite emphasis on defensive and aggressive activities alerts management to the broad trend of corporate technology.

Finally, the objective approach to matching potential benefits against use of technical resources creates an atmosphere of logical analysis appropriate to leadership of a professional staff. Judgments are reached through reasoning processes rather than through dictatorial hunches. While internal opinions may differ on details of evaluation, this type of decision making creates confidence of strong leadership by demonstrating clarity of purpose and policy.

CHAPTER 7   ORGANIZATION
OF TECHNICAL
DEPARTMENTS

Purpose of an Organization

The theory for establishing an organization is that it represents the chain of command through which activities at lower echelons are planned, assigned, supervised, approved, and summarized for transmittal through administrative channels. The relationships are often defined by organization charts, such as those shown later in this chapter.

The need for clarification of relationships among members of an organization develops as the size increases and as the functions to be performed become differentiated into specialized categories. It is obvious that, although a one-man craft operation may be completely self-contained, a two-man operation with one man manufacturing and the other marketing must involve a meeting of the minds as to what is to be made that can be sold, for otherwise even this simple enterprise will fail. Passing from this elementary stage to the giant industrial enterprises of today calls for progressively complex means for defining, subdividing, and assigning responsibilities for the functions to be performed.

In a formal organization, with rigid lines of communication, the carrying out of the successive stages and steps in product or process development would require procedures for reporting and coordinating results on individual phases which would be so time-consuming that the commercial goal would be reached very slowly. In practice, even in a large organization, some intermediate channels of communication - such as review or coordinating committees - are necessary. In operations that are repetitive, such as routine manufacturing of standardized products, a master plan can be developed from which work assignments and supervision can be administered according to formula, but even here the execution must be flexible enough to take into account the human element. When the objective involves creativity, however, because the facts are not known but must be discovered and synthesized into the form of a unified whole, the planning cannot be complete enough to encompass all the technical possibilities in advance. In other words, it is not feasible to dictate to a scientist or engineer the details of how he is to invent a new product, device, or process.

Research and development activities are still further complicated by the high degree of specialization in different parts of the organization. For this reason it can come about that in a large research department a problem which requires the joint efforts of an organic chemist and a physicist will find these men quite widely separated on the organization chart, and often they may be working in locations at considerable distance from each other. Obviously, their contributions must be brought to a common focus, and while this might be accomplished through an intermediary at a common higher echelon, this can be an inefficient method of operation.

Multi-disciplinary teams or task forces are, therefore, being used to increasing extent by successful research and development organizations as a direct means of assembling a variety of skills for a common purpose. This is a device for operating on specific assignments through an "informal organization," although the necessity for a "formal organization" for administrative purposes still exists. The procedures for organizing and operating task forces will be discussed in detail in later chapters.

Formal Plan of Organization

Small Organizations, in which the channels of communication are short, are less subject to problems of obtaining interdisciplinary cooperation. The manager of technical activities is in frequent contact with the managing director and with the heads of the operating departments. He is also in continual contact with the small number of technical men in his department. Therefore, he should be able to operate effectively in coordination with manufacturing and marketing and at the same time directly supervise the technical work, the results of which he transmits to them in appropriate manner to suit the occasion. If he needs to arrange for plant trials of a new product or process, he steps across the hall to talk to the manager of manufacturing. If he wishes to obtain the opinion of the manager of marketing about the suitability of a product for distribution, he takes a few steps to another office to see him. There is much less need for detailed reports to submit through channels.

A typical organization chart of the situation is given in Figure 3. The technical department may in some cases report to the manager of manufacturing or the manager of marketing, instead of to the general manager, but direct relationship to the general manager is preferable. In such a small organization it is easy for the key figures of the company to get together for discussion. "Management meetings," whether on a formal or informal schedule, give the technical manager an easy route to discuss the status of his projects.

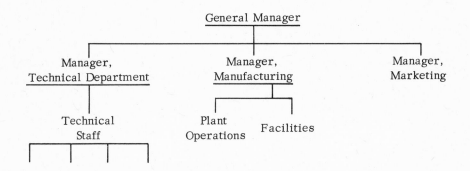

FIGURE 3   ORGANIZATION CHART OF A SMALL COMPANY

Medium-sized Organizations tend toward greater specialization, and the technical director often finds it advisable to split the laboratory-oriented work into a "research section," while the larger-scale work is in a "development section," with himself as the director and coordinator of the two activities. The department may grow large enough, however, so that he will need to appoint a manager of research and a manager of development, each having responsibility for organizing and supervising his staff. (See Figure 4.)

Even in an enterprise of intermediate size, the channels of communication have often lengthened to such an extent that it is difficult for the technical director to check with the operating departments and top management at frequent intervals.

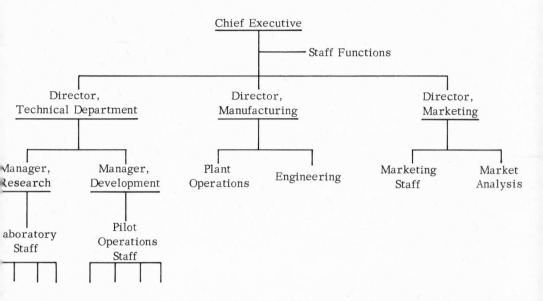

FIGURE 4   ORGANIZATION CHART OF A MEDIUM-SIZED COMPANY

Large Organizations necessarily require that research and development activities be still further divided. There may be a section doing oriented
long-range research. It is likely that the applied laboratory work will be split
into sections, either according to disciplines (such as organic chemistry, in-
organic chemistry, physics, and biology), into product groups, or into a combination of the two types. The development activities will be subdivided into still
other specialized activities (such as project analysis, process engineering, and
pilot plant operation). In larger laboratory operations the need for staff functions
increases and these may come under such headings as planning and evaluation,
personnel administration, facilities and maintenance, and library and information.

Communications between research and development and the rest of the
organization will have become still more diffuse. Special working committees
may be set up for purposes of communication and coordination at lower echelons.
Finally, it should be mentioned that the research and development department

will have grown to such a size that it may have to be housed in separate quarters at some distance from the headquarters of the company and from the centers of manufacturing and marketing.

Figure 5 illustrates how such an organization might look.

There are still more complicated organizations in which research and development functions are further subdivided to correspond to corporate "divisions," each of which handles manufacturing and marketing for a separate product line. In some cases these divisions have their own research and development departments. A corporate technical director may be appointed to serve as coordinator, in order to insure interchange of information among the division technical groups. Sometimes a corporate research program is established for the purpose of undertaking the necessary research and development leading to new product lines or new businesses, while the divisional technical programs concentrate in their respective areas. This type of organization presents the hazard that the technical programs of the divisions, which are usually profit centers and therefore very cost-conscious, may gravitate toward short-term activities, while the corporate research program becomes longer and longer in range. The difficulties of handling the situation have resulted in many cases in cycles of emphasis on centralized control alternating with decentralization of research and development. A major risk is that intermediate-range projects may be neglected because they fall between the areas of interest of divisional and corporate technical departments.

Technical Coordination Committees

To overcome the difficulties of long lines of communication in larger organizations, various committees are often used. In most companies these are advisory groups and not management committees. The philosophy is quite generally accepted that management by committee does not lead to forceful decision making; the tendency is to place responsibility for decisions in a given area in a single executive, with advice and communication effected through committee activity, either formal or informal.

Technical Policy Committees at management level are often established for discussion of general policy and program for research and development. The chairman may be the technical director or the general manager, and senior executives of manufacturing and marketing serve as members, along with other staff officers whose counsel may be helpful.

Technical Advisory Committees may be used to secure the advice of senior technical personnel and representatives of operating departments, as well as to keep them informed of the status of the program. The technical director normally serves as chairman.

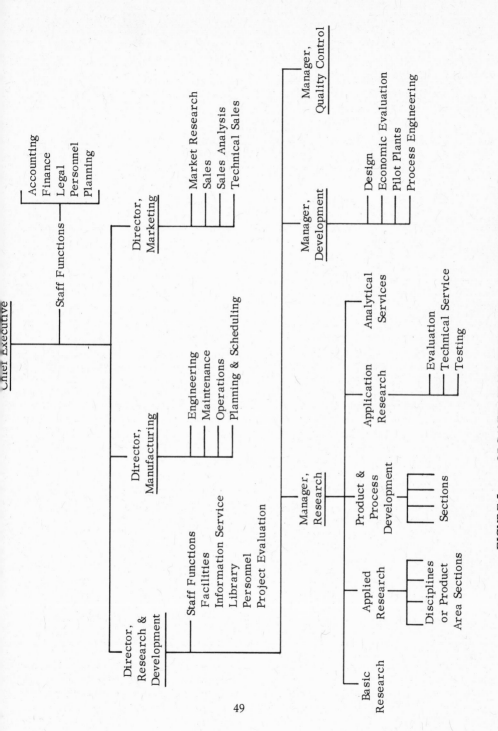

Chief Executive

Staff Functions
— Accounting
— Finance
— Legal
— Personnel
— Planning

Director, Research & Development
Director, Manufacturing
Director, Marketing

Director, Marketing
— Market Research
— Sales
— Sales Analysis
— Technical Sales

Director, Manufacturing
— Engineering
— Maintenance
— Operations
— Planning & Scheduling

Director, Research & Development
— Staff Functions
— Facilities
— Information Service
— Library
— Personnel
— Project Evaluation

Manager, Research

Basic Research

Applied Research
— Disciplines or Product Area Sections

Product & Process Development
— Sections

Application Research
— Evaluation
— Technical Service
— Testing

Analytical Services

Manager, Development
— Design
— Economic Evaluation
— Pilot Plants
— Process Engineering

Manager, Quality Control

49

FIGURE 5   ORGANIZATION CHART OF A LARGE COMPANY

Operation of Coordinating Committees. Efficient procedures for operation of bodies of this type are very important. To avoid wastage of valuable executive time and ennui caused by unproductive long discussions, the following general rules should be helpful:

1. Regular schedule of meetings, including estimate of time involved;
2. Advance distribution of agenda with back-up information memoranda where available;
3. Forceful chairmanship, either on continuing or rotating basis;
4. Appointment of sub-committees or task forces to review and make recommendations on topics of divided opinion or of limited interest to many members;
5. Preparation and distribution of minutes;
6. Follow-up of decisions reached.

Echelons in Technical Organizations

In larger organizations there is an ever-present danger that the number of administrative layers will retard progress and stifle creativity. Results from the laboratory move up through the echelons, which are progressively handicapped by lack of direct contact with the work. Comments and decisions filter down again to the working level with all the frustrations that are predictable. Multiple echelons are not desirable from the point of view of rapid creation and implementation of new technology. Task force operation counteracts the inhibitions of a rigid organization with many layers of authority and responsibility.

The Informal Working Organization

Accepting as we do the need of a formal organization for administrative purposes (including staffing, establishing general policies for work, personnel administration, assignment of problems, general supervision of work, disciplinary action, etc.), how can the multi-disciplinary task force system be superimposed in order to focus on each project the proper admixture of technical talent?

First of all, to prevent a chaotic and confusing situation, a regular system of project outlines must be instituted. Such outlines, normally prepared after a suitable exploratory study, should give the objective of the phase of the problem to be covered, the justification for undertaking it, the general approach in the technical work, the estimate of time required, a table of diversified manpower needed, and estimated expense. The project is then placed under the leadership of one of the experienced men, who is given responsibility for assembling the team of necessary talents from various parts of the organization, assigning their functions in the investigation, supervising the manner in which they carry out these assignments, and reporting results. The assignments are often for limited periods of time and for part-time participation. The ground rules under which the project leader secures these services from various parts of the organization have to be understood and accepted by the respective supervisors whose men may be involved, and of course by the men themselves.

This may sound like an operating procedure foreign to the normal way of carrying out technical programs, but it is being practiced successsfully in many laboratories in the United States. It is often employed by other companies in cases of crisis; even in organizations which adhere to a formal method of operation, a task force will be assembled to provide a solution to an emergency problem and upon solution the members will go back to their former system of operation.

Later on we will discuss in more detail how such a task force system operates, but it seems timely to point out that it is very beneficial for stimulating professional motivation and creativity. The project leader must use his best efforts to develop a sense of responsibility and participation on the part of all members of the team. Just as in team sports, he must set the direction of play but do it in such a way that the best efforts of his mates are called for. While the team leader must take responsibility for major decisions and must supervise the performance of the individual participants, he should encourage them to think for themselves and to feel free to express their opinions. Two environmental factors encourage this attitude: (1) Since specialists from various disciplines are involved, he is unlikely to feel that he is as proficient as they in their respective fields and is therefore led to encouragement of their independent views, a relationship which should prove contagious for the rest of the team. (2) Members are selected for the team in a sort of "volunteer" arrangement, because of their interest in the project and mutual belief that they can contribute, with the result that the team leader has a relationship with them quite different from that of organizational chain of command.

Extra-Mural Research Projects

The subject of external projects appears to be particularly pertinent to the situation in developing economies as a means of enabling individual enterprises or industry groups to benefit from the important technical resources often concentrated in Government laboratories. The long experience in America and the trend toward contract research now developing in Europe, as well as recent developments in other countries that are not yet highly industrialized, all point to the potential value of this method of obtaining technical help.

In America, industrial companies now spend an average of about four percent of their research budgets on extra-mural projects. These are carried out in independent laboratories, industrial research institutes, and university laboratories. Organizations such as ADL and Mellon Institute, founded in 1886 and 1913 respectively, paved the way to the expansion of such activities following World War I, and the spectacular rate of growth during and after World War II. The latest year for which comprehensive data are available is 1953; at that time a survey revealed 12 research institutes with combined annual budgets from sponsors of $53 million and 6,000 employees. The same survey covered 175 commercial laboratories with a total income of $24 million.

Major reasons for using extra-mural projects are the flexibility and speed of obtaining expertise not available in the company, the advantage of a fresh approach to problems, relief from over-load of work facing the company technical staff, confirmation of results and opinions by an impartial group, and stimulation of internal technical morale through outside contacts. A basic factor in the success is the joint motivation shared by the sponsor and the extra-mural group in attacking a well-defined project.

Adoption of contract research in Western Europe is a more recent phenomenon, and hitherto more dependence was placed on research associations made up of companies in a sector of industry; national policy has favored such laboratories, and in many countries they are in part financed by the Government. As an example of the trend toward contract research, in the United Kingdom, where research associations began to flourish over 40 years ago and sponsored research was virtually unknown until recent years, eight contract laboratories are now receiving about £2 million per year, a sum one-third the size of the contributions made by industry to the 52 Research Association laboratories. It should be noted also that in Great Britain and other European countries the policy is developing of offering to do work in Research Association and Government-supported laboratories on a contract basis for individual firms.

Here and there in less developed countries contract research organizations are arising, sometimes with government support, sometimes under private operation. It is safe to prophesy that growth of this movement will be steady.

CHAPTER 8

BASIC
RESEARCH

Fundamental Research in Academic Institutions

In Western countries the idea of establishing scientific status by carrying out and publishing the results of independent researches began to assume importance a century ago.

Each country developed a system for recognizing scientific prestige to suit its own culture, and there was considerable difference among nations in the requirements. In Germany, high status was accorded to men who had received a doctorate, and many American and British scientists in the later years of the 19th century and still more in the first decades of the 20th century received research training in that country. As a result of experience with this system, American postgraduate requirements leading to the Ph.D. degree followed the German system to considerable extent, with modifications to adapt it to the local situation.

In France and Great Britain, on the other hand, the doctorate was usually sought at a later stage in professional career, and it carried special significance in those countries; submission of a thesis was postponed until the candiate was ready to submit a report on a particularly notable investigation. Since World War I, more students from abroad have sought advanced training in Great Britain and France and they have felt the need for some form of academic recognition; this resulted in the widespread award of the Ph.D. in Britain and a doctorate with modified requirements in France.

In all countries the emphasis was on the completion and publication of an original investigation on some subject selected by the candidate and his research advisor. The choice bore no relationship to practical implications, and in some circles problems with applied overtones were shunned because practicality was believed to detract from theoretical significance. It was a recognized tenet that the purpose of a doctorate thesis was to add to the sum total of scientific knowledge and that the conduct of such work was evidence of original thinking and hence the best training for an academic career.

Sponsored Research in American Universities

Much concern has been expressed in the United States about the growing trend in universities to accept sponsored projects with defined objectives, even though these be legitimate scientific goals. From the academic point of view, research of this type lacks the spontaneity and complete freedom of choice appropriate to the spirit of inquiry of an educational institution.

Industrial sponsorship of projects in universitites began before World
War I. The Industrial Fellowship system, started by Dr. Duncan at the University
of Kansas in 1907, later transferred to the University of Pittsburgh, and in 1913
incorporated in Mellon Institute, called attention to its advantages. Several other
research institutes, notably at Illionois (formerly Armour) Institute of Technology and Leland Stanford University, were organized within the general framework
of a university.

The practice of using professors as consultants and of placing investigations under them continued to grow between the two World Wars. Also a number of companies established post-graduate fellowships and unrestricted research
grants, which were more highly esteemed by the academic world.

During World War II, large numbers of university faculty members
became involved in the practical problems resulting from wartime emergency,
either through service in the National Defense Research Committee program or
through conducting projects in their own institutions, some of the latter becoming
very large. At the end of the war, the attractive possibility remained of obtaining funds from Government agencies or industry for supporting research when
the academic men returned to their normal university activities. The Office of
Naval Research pioneered in allocating funds for fundamental work, and other
agencies became active on a similar basis.

The volume of research thus supported has grown enormously, but the
academic world believes the trend is hazardous. The same question is being
raised in the United Kingdom, because university professors have begun to accept
research contracts. In Germany, Switzerland, and some other countries in
Western Europe, however, cooperation between industry or Government and
members of the technical faculties has enjoyed a long history of success and is
not regarded with suspicion.

Postgraduate Training in Developing Economies

Because most institutions in the less highly developed countries were
not prepared to offer postgraduate courses leading to the doctorate, selected
students have been sent abroad in increasing number to obtain their advanced
scientific training. As they have returned to their native countries, in many
cases to posts in university faculties, the opportunities for them to put their
scientific attainments to use in indoctrinating local students has grown and will
undoubtedly expand to higher levels. The doctorates awarded in these countries
will gradually approach in prestige those from foreign institutions, although
doubtless there will remain an aura of elegance about overseas scientific experience.

The scientific research carried out locally by post-graduate students will begin to be a strong force in the educational system of the country. There has been considerable opinion voiced, however, that, because of the limited supply of highly trained scientists in developing countries, it is not in the national interest to select research projects with the same freedom from practical significance which exists in the more advanced nations. Surely there is some merit in these views, but, at the same time, if training in local universities is to provide a means of developing highly skilled scientists, rigorous requirements for theoretical content of the research projects must be maintained. This should not be an insoluble dilemma. In considering the subject of fundamental research in developing countries, it is suggested that one approach might be along the lines of that which has developed in American and European industries in their basic research programs in order to attract scientists of high attainments.

Basic Research in American Industry

Many prominent American and European companies began to establish long-range research several decades ago. Bell Laboratories, du Pont, and General Electric in the United States; I.G. Farben in Germany; St. Gobain in France; and I.C.I. in Britain, to name some outstanding examples, pioneered in this respect. In quite a number of instances, important new areas of technology grew out of such scientific work, which was in theoretical importance on a par with the fundamental research carried out in universities. Results of much of the work found their way into journals devoted to publication of "pure" science.

Many more companies followed the route of sponsoring basic research projects in universities or other scientific institutions. This not only had the advantage of providing a means for long-range investigation of problems in their areas of interest, but also it was considered to be an appropriate policy on the part of firms to make a contribution to the sum total of scientific knowledge, from which reservoir they are continually drawing information for application to their practical problems. In some cases, basic work is sponsored through industry organizations such as American Petroleum Institute, Corn Industries Research Foundation, and Nutrition Foundation, to which individual companies make contributions.

There has been a strong trend upward in the United States since World War II in the support of basic research by industry. The publication "Basic Research in the Navy," which reports the results of a study carried out by an ADL team in 1958-59 on behalf of the U.S. Naval Research Advisory Committee, summarizes the policies of 33 leading companies, representing the source of almost one-fifth of the nation's and one-half of industry's total basic research funds. The percentage of total research and development budgets devoted to basic research programs by 20 companies had roughly doubled in the decade

1947-57. Ten corporations--two each from the fields of chemicals, petroleum, communications-electronic, pharmaceuticals, and materials--had a minimum of ten percent and a maximum of 20 percent allocated to basic research, the average being about 16 percent. Fourteen leading companies increased basic research expenditures by a factor of 4.5 during the decade, while their total research and development budgets tripled. Obviously these companies believe that applied research and development proceed more rapidly when closely backed by basic research.

In other countries different procedures were adopted. In Great Britain, for example, after World War I the Government encouraged various industries to establish Research Association laboratories, of which there are now over 50, and in making contributions from the public purse felt that part of this financial help would be used for basic research, while the more applied types of work would be supported chiefly through contributions from industrial members of the associations. The research association and cooperative research concepts have spread in some form or other to a dozen countries of Western Europe, although they are undergoing modification.

Serendipity in Basic Research

Some credence and considerably more "lip service" have been given to the concept that if a company recruits a group of competent scientists and leaves them free to work on any problem they choose, important technologic breakthroughs will result in due course: all one needs is patience. This theory is frequently referred to as "serendipity," that is, good fortune by accident.

Experience in the United States has greatly reduced reliance on the concept of serendipity. Instead, emphasis is now in the direction appropriately called "oriented long-range research."

Two years ago one of the financial papers wished to publish an article on the importance of chance discoveries - serendipity - in producing technologic breakthroughs for the companies that supported the basic work. Some members of ADL cooperated by trying to find case histories to support the story. A quite broad search revealed, however, that the number of important accidental discoveries was disappointingly small. Most of the examples that turned up through superficial screening turned out, when objectively evaluated, to be based on planned programs for exploring technical areas of interest to the company, with potential application as the ultimate objective.

Oriented Long-Range Research

Other lines of thinking have become prevalent in larger research organizations in recent years. Among these is the recognition that even a very large company can conduct in its own laboratory only a very small part of the fundamental research pertinent to its field of operations. This means, therefore, that the company has little chance of uncovering through its own work the exact items of new information which will have significance in its future technology. On the other hand, a competent research man working in a given scientific area must necessarily keep thoroughly abreast of what is going on in the rest of the scientific world. This leads to the conclusion that the basic research staff should serve as a window looking toward the sum total of knowledge, and be able to interpret and call to the attention of the applied research men new discoveries anywhere in the world that may have significance. This type of liaison has been called "coupling between basic research and technology."

This idea leads to the question of what areas of science a company should select in order that it may have an appropriate liaison program. Research organizations are, therefore, seeking to analyze those scientific fields which may be important to them in their operations five years, ten, or even further ahead. They are trying to establish a spectrum of areas of scientific interest, to staff these areas for liaison, and to support basic research on the part of the staff in order that they may be in continual communication with other scientists working in their fields of specialization.

An additional idea that is being applied in establishing a program of basic research is to attempt to identify barrier problems hindering long-range advances in technology, for which there is not yet sufficient scientific information to foresee the directions of solutions. Application of this method of thinking is, of course, a procedure to assist in definition of the scientific spectrum of interest.

It should be emphasized again that the research conducted on these long-range problems is often of very high standards and that the results are accepted for publication in recognized journals of pure science.

The philosophy of oriented long-range research is reassuring also to the scientists. Many of them in basic research laboratories in industry, while well content with the stimulating atmosphere and working conditions, eventually begin to be concerned about the dichotomy of being supported in "pure" science by a company whose aim is to conduct a profitable business. Emphasis on the function of screening the world reservoir of science to uncover areas of technologic breakthrough provides them with a sense of playing a part in reaching corporate objectives.

There remain many problems in administering these activities effectively. The establishment of good channels of liaison between basic and applied
scientists is by no means simple. To the author one of the best procedures is
to include the basic researchers as consultants on appropriate product and process development teams.

Oriented Long-Range Research in Developing Countries

It seems logical that this experience on the part of American industry,
which is not unique in this respect but also resembles the reasoning adopted by
the foremost companies in other countries, may point in a direction pertinent to
the scientific philosophy of developing economies. Admitting the value of fundamental research as a training procedure for younger scientists, is it not possible
to employ the principles of oriented long-range research in industry? If those
responsible for assisting students to select research projects in candidacy for
higher degrees will keep in mind the relationships of the subjects to the national
interest, it should be possible to choose problems of requisite scientific content
and still pertinent to national development. To carry out such a program there
is need for formulation of a scientific spectrum relating to the broad needs of
the country.

This suggested approach does not detract, it should be emphasized,
from the depth of scientific inquiry represented by a project selected on this
basis. It does not prejudice the acceptance of the results for publication in
recognized journals; if wisely conducted, it is not opposed to the principles of
academic freedom. On the other hand, it should give the scientists from developing countries the additional gratification of working on subjects that have
potential value in their own national economies. Finally, and perhaps most important of all, the scientists will become acquainted in their respective areas
with fundamental research in selected fields in their own and in other countries,
and will serve the purpose of scientific liaison, to which so much importance is
attached by companies in industrialized countries.

CHAPTER **9**   PRODUCT
AND PROCESS
DEVELOPMENT

Stages and Steps in Development

This chapter outlines the sequence of stages and steps involved in carrying a product idea from conception to commercialization. It emphasizes the product rather than the process, because most companies are oriented in this direction and relatively few are primarily concerned with selling processes.

This presentation is directed toward the means by which the skills of the organization are focused on three basic questions:

Marketing feasibility - Is it worth making?

Technical feasibility - Can it be made practically?

Economic feasibility - Will it pay its way?

Results from initial stages usually give a reliable answer as to technical feasibility, a preliminary estimate of market potential, and a rough idea of economics. Further work is concerned with perfection of technology, confirmation of market demand, and compilation of economic data to permit managerial decision regarding commercialization.

A few decades ago new products and processes were often developed, even in large companies, through the initiative of a single individual acting as an entrepreneur within the organization. He was successively inventor, developer, production manager, and marketer, and often became general manager of the operation. This frequently happens today in smaller enterprises, particularly in science-based industries such as electronics.

In larger companies, however, size and specialization of functions have lead to assignment of responsibilities to different departments and groups. In many mature industries, the simpler things have been done, and complex problems require a diversity of skills for implementation. In the search for new opportunities, momentum may be lost, and this slowing up is often blamed on reduced creativity in research. A major problem in administration, therefore, is the stimulation of a diverse group of specialists to function as a dynamic entrepreneur in originating product ideas, evaluating them speedily, and translating the good ones into successful business ventures.

The outline of stages starts with an innovative idea for which a framework of applicability has to be worked out. An item closely related to an existing product line obviously will not require the detailed initial investigation outlined for an innovative new product. The sequence of steps will vary from case to case, but radical departure from the scale of study (e.g., premature expansion to large pilot plant) may lead to wasted effort, although the risk may be justified by the possibility of speeding up the development.

The outline as given is built around a hypothetical product in the process industries, i.e., chemical and related manufactures, foods, petroleum products, paper, etc. By suitable change in terms - notably design department and model shop instead of laboratory work - it can be adapted to products in the mechanical-electrical field.

The major steps are numbered in sequence to facilitate reference.

Basic Research

In the laboratory group devoted to oriented long-range research, one line of investigation reveals a compound with unusual properties which appear to deserve exploration. The discovery may have resulted from an attack based on theoretical reasoning that substances of this type would show certain behaviors, or it may have arisen through study of some set of phenomena whose parameters were being tested by use of different materials. In any case, it is judged to lie in an area of scientific interest of the company, and a broader research approach is made to round out knowledge by testing related compounds under varying conditions.

The steps are:

1. Discovery of a new phenomenon

2. Decision that it may lie in the broad area of interest of the company

3. Exploration of the parameters of the phenomenon

Applied Research

In the course of liaison between basic and applied research, a specific idea arises for applying the phenomenon to the company's technology. Responsibility for analyzing the possibility further is assigned to a man in the applied research laboratory. He reviews the work in basic research, and he also seeks comments from specialists in appropriate product development groups. Initial screening tests may be carried out to sharpen definition of requirements for application. The invention has not become sufficiently explicit to permit economic justification; it can only be stated that the phenomenon is believed to have utility of considerable importance in an area of industry of interest to the company. An applied research project is authorized to prepare a wider series of related compounds in order to evaluate their performance in preliminary use tests.

The steps are:

4. Initial idea of utility

5. Preliminary exploration to test the concept

6. Authorization of an applied research project to:

    A. Develop screening methodology, define potential commercial advantages;

    B. Work out practical laboratory methods of preparation;

    C. Prepare and evaluate a series of compounds by the screening procedures;

    D. Recommend one or more products for further development.

Product Development

On the basis of preliminary evidence of utility of one or more potential products which can be made by what appears to be a practical procedure, a man in product development is assigned responsibility for pulling together technical and economic information as a project proposal, including estimates of professional time involved, total cost, and target date. At this stage the economic questions do not require or warrant investigation in depth: they can usually be answered with sufficient accuracy, by expenditure of a few days of effort, from information and experience now available within the company. If a major negative factor appears, however, its bearing should be analyzed in more depth before the new project is authorized.

When the plan of work has been approved, the method of preparation is studied systematically on a small scale. Then samples of the products for internal evaluation are prepared by the preferred procedures, which should be regarded as prototypes of commercial manufacture, to avoid the error of carrying out tests on materials with properties different from those that might be offered commercially. Preliminary consideration is given to handling and packaging problems. Evaluation is carried out by existing or specially devised test methods. Further review is made of marketing problems and estimated costs as additional information is accumulated.

7. Product definition and preliminary evaluations

    A. Performance requirements - general

    B. Raw materials - general, availability and cost

    C. Preparation of small samples of preferred composition

    D. Initial confirmation of technical evaluation on preferred samples

    E. Initial economic evaluation

        a. Market size and type
        b. Distribution system - general
        c. Rough cost estimate (often derived from raw material costs by a factor based on experience with related materials)
        d. Competitive situation - general
        e. Pertinent patents and licenses
        f. Minimum economic scale of production

8. Product development proposal

    A. Summary of data from 7

    B. Recommendation for project, including time and cost estimates to complete the following steps:

        a. Screening program
        b. Product sample preparation
        c. Internal evaluation
        d. Readiness for process development

    C. Submission and approval of proposal

9. Preparation of small-scale samples

    A. Selection of materials, including special ingredients

    B. Examination of methodology from standpoint of manufacturing feasibility

    C. Determination of stability and storage requirements

    D. Procedures for quality control

    E. Initial packaging concept

    F. Review of process flow diagram

    G. Preparation of representative samples for internal evaluation.

10. Internal evaluation of product

    A. Selection and development of test methods

    B. Performance evaluation of representative samples

    C. Cost review with engineering evaluation group

    D. Market review with market research group

    E. Comparison with competitive products

    F. Initial evaluations of special character such as use or shipping hazards, types of customer specifications, etc.

11. Establishment of tentative product specifications

Process Development and Field Evaluation

The preceding phase has rounded out knowledge of the product and its performance, has confirmed potential marketability insofar as this can be determined by internal evaluation, and has established a tentative flow sheet for manufacturing process. The present stage is concerned with: (a) re-evaluating the technical and economic feasibility on a large laboratory or pre-pilot scale; (b) extending evaluation to small-scale tests in customers' plants or in consumer groups; (c) making a preliminary outline of the marketing plan.

12. Proposal for process development

    A. Summary of information from product development stage

    B. Recommendation for project, including time and cost estimates to complete:

        a. Final process selection
        b. Completion of process definition by intermediate scale work
        c. Availability of samples for field tests
        d. Preliminary estimates of timing and cost for installation and operation of pilot facilities

    C. Submission and approval of proposal, which may be conditional on proposal for field evaluation.

13.   Process development

A.   Re-evaluation of laboratory preparation in terms of technology, materials of construction, operating cost, and plant investment projected to commercial scale

B.   Assembly of prototype small equipment (pre-pilot scale)

C.   Perfection of process on prototype operation

D.   Confirmation of technical and economic feasibility on basis of new information

E.   Preparation of samples for field tests

14.   Field evaluation

A.   Schedule of tests and samples required and review of details with market development group and marketing department

B.   Development of final information regarding special tests, if required, such as safety, Government regulations, customer specifications, etc.

C.   Compilation of information on techniques for use by customers

D.   Confirmation of market acceptability by customer tests

E.   Detailed review of tentative product specifications

F.   Re-evaluation of merchandising concepts

G.   Confirmation of proposed marketing approach

H.   Development of preliminary outline for technical bulletins, labels, containers, shipping requirements, etc.

Pilot Plant Operation and Market Tests

All preceding work has been on a relatively small scale, with proportionately small investment of time and money. Insofar as possible, all basic problems should have been worked out, with a view to using pilot plant and market test only to confirm the doubtful points. If new problems arise regarding process, product specifications, or performance, they should be referred back to the product and process development groups to attempt to find initial solutions on a small scale.

15. Proposal for pilot plant and market testing

    A. Comprehensive review of process technology and economics

    B. Comprehensive review of product specifications, field test results, and internal evaluations

    C. Preparation of proposal for pilot plant work, including time and cost schedule for:

        a. Design of pilot plant
        b. First draft of quality control program
        c. Installation of pilot plant
        d. Operation on pilot scale
        e. Timing and cost of samples for market tests
        f. Preliminary estimate of investment and operating costs of commercial plant

16. Design and installation of pilot plant

    A. Definition of process details

    B. Review of possibility of integration with present commercial processes

    C. Scale up to pilot design

        a. Materials of construction
        b. Flexibility of design for engineering determinations
        c. Special techniques required
        d. Plan for testing and evaluation of product with manufacturing and sales departments
        e. Coordination with engineering department
        f. Program for training operators

    D. Review of problems of by-product and waste disposal

    E. Program for systematic process evaluation, to analyze data in order to optimize operating conditions and cost relationships

    F. Detailed design of pilot plant

    G. Installation of pilot facilities

    H. First draft of plant operating manual

17.   Operation of pilot facilities

    A. Training of operating crew

    B. Elimination of process variables

    C. Correlation of operation with manufacturing department

    D. Production of samples for market tests

    E. Re-evaluation of products, by-products, wastes, and costs

    F. Revision of operating manual

    G. Confirmation of quality control program

    H. Recommendations regarding design of commercial facility, including site requirements, waste problems, special facilities, and semi-final cost estimates

18.   Market tests

    A. Selection of test areas

    B. Final review of market test plan

    C. Operation of market tests

    D. Review of test data

    E. Preparation of complete merchandising and marketing program and preliminary budgets

    F. First drafts of sales agreements or contracts

Comprehensive Review Preparatory to Commercialization

At this vital stage, all matters relating to the success of the commercial venture should be brought to a common focus. Insofar as it is feasible to do so, all departments and groups concerned should be alerted to the important step about to be taken so that no pertinent factors will be overlooked. The inquiry should extend as far back as applied research or even basic research. In the time elapsed since they were directly concerned with the project, has any new information come to light which has a bearing on product or process?

19. <u>Preparation of recommendation for commercialization</u>

    A. Final review and confirmation

        a. Technology
        b. Flow diagram for commercial plant
        c. Investment and operating costs
        d. Marketing and advertising programs

    B. Preparation of schedule and expense estimate for

        a. Final design of plant
        b. Installation of facilities
        c. Regular operation
        d. Initiation of marketing

    C. Decision to commercialize

Initial Steps for Commercialization

20. <u>Final site selection</u>

    A. Marketing considerations

    B. Raw materials

    C. Transportation

    D. Location-imposed restrictions such as taxes, waste disposal, etc.

    E. Availability of labor

    F. Availability of specialized staff

    G. Land availability and cost

21. <u>Final review</u> of market, costs, pricing, estimated profit, competition, distribution, etc., to justify decision for plant construction

22. <u>Detailed design of facilities</u>

Implementation of Commercial Project

23. <u>Construction of facility</u>

24.   Manufacturing staff activities

A.   Training of supervisors and operators

B.   Final draft of operating manual

C.   Final draft of quality control procedures

25.   Mobilization of sales and promotion

A.   Preparation of advertising and promotional material

B.   Sales training program

C.   Negotiation of sales agreements and contracts

26.   Tune-in period, to confirm satisfactory design and construction of plant, and suitability of product, process,
and control procedure

27.   Acceptance of operation for regular manufacture and sales,
and establishment of normal schedule for quality control and
technical service.

CHAPTER **10**   ENGINEERING
DEVELOPMENT
FUNCTIONS

Scope and Coordination

Engineering development functions include: establishment of engineering parameters of the basic technology for a process, proving its feasibility for large-scale operation on pilot scale, specifying the necessary equipment and layout for commercial plant, evaluating the economics of production, and assisting the manufacturing department in installing and starting up the operation.

Because many of the activities become specialized in a large organization, they are often carried out by separate groups. Even in a small organization, where subdivision of engineering responsibilities is not complex, it is helpful to recognize the different aspects of work involved. This helps to define responsibility for engineering participation at the stages and steps listed in the preceding chapter.

The specialized engineering activities may be located at various places in the organization, which may lead to problems in communication. Generally speaking, however, coordination is not too difficult to establish, because engineers tend to express themselves in ways that are mutually understood, although differences in professional approaches and opinions have to be reconciled.

Definitions of Engineering Functions

Process development is concerned with definition in engineering terms of information from laboratory or model shop work for the series of operating steps necessary to carry out manufacture on a commercial scale.

Process engineering is concerned with analysis of flow diagrams and equipment specifications for proposed processes and installations, including transfer of materials and energy, to insure technical success and operating efficiency.

Techno-economic evaluation is the systematic projection of cost estimates for stepping up smaller-scale data to semi-works or commercial operations. The scope of analysis includes calculation of costs of facilities and manufacturing procedures in order to formulate the economic factors to be used by management, together with estimates of sales and profits, in reaching decisions regarding the implementation of proposed undertakings.

Design engineering deals with the detailed drawings and specifications for facilities, equipment, machinery, and auxiliaries in a form suitable for fabrication for the required purpose.

Project engineering denotes the responsibility for implementing process design - including plot plans, flow of materials diagrams, and controls and instrumentation - by overseeing detailed specifications for purchase or fabrication of equipment, and by supervising installation and initial tune-in period of plant.

Step-Wise Process Development

Laboratory results or prototype models give evidence that an initial idea is technically feasible, but the information has been obtained without thorough analysis of the procedures that would be involved in large-scale manufacture. The following discussion is directed at the process industries, including chemicals, foods, petroleum, and the like, but the philosophy is also applicable to operations involved in the mechanical-electrical industries.

Laboratory studies are usually carried out in glassware to prove that the transformations in composition and form of the materials take place under conditions judged to be practical, and with an efficiency that is believed to be in economic range.

As a first step toward the development of commercial undertakings, the laboratory findings have to be confirmed in a program that takes into consideration: (1) the types and materials of construction of equipment to be procured or fabricated for the operation; (2) the performance of commercially available raw materials; (3) the requirements for introducing components in controlled amounts and conditions; (4) the limitations on production conditions; (5) the methodology for isolating the product in satisfactory yield and quality; and (6) the handling of by-products and wastes.

These trials to establish commercial feasibility may be made in several steps, for example, large glassware, pre-pilot plant (sometimes called "desk top units"), pilot plant study of critical steps, pilot plant for total operation, and semi-works plant. Each successive step becomes considerably more expensive and involved in terms of equipment, raw materials consumed, and calculation of mass and energy balances. A rule-of-thumb scale-up policy for innovative operations is often set at not more than a ten-fold increase in size at each step; in the case of modifications of existing processes, this ratio is normally unduly conservative.

Development steps should be so planned as to obtain the information on the smallest scale of experimentation that is feasible, thus insuring that exploratory work and unproductive trials or mistakes are made on minimum size. Larger-scale work (e.g., pilot plant runs) should be used to confirm findings of earlier steps rather than to "research" them, and should be used for research only when it is not possible to extrapolate information from smaller-scale experimentation with required accuracy. This demands thorough analysis of the results of small-scale investigation to determine whether it is necessary to carry the work to a larger stage, and if so, to decide what types of new information can be gained and by what procedures.

The results of process development are usually summarized in a preliminary flow diagram, which incorporates information obtained regarding sizes and construction of equipment, transfer of materials, operating conditions, instrumentation and control procedures, etc.

Pilot plants are often left in stand-by condition after the original program of work has been completed, so that they can be used for investigation of new problems that arise later on.

Pilot Plants as Small-Scale Production Units

Superficially it is often assumed that a pilot plant can be usefully employed for regular production of small quantities of products to fill special orders or during the period before commercial operation is started on a new product. From the point of view of economics, this is generally a false assumption, because application of normal accounting procedures will show very high production costs.

Pilot plants are usually considerably below minimum economic size. Because they are planned as experimental units, they have a built-in flexibility that requires abnormal attention to process control, and the operating crew is likely to be heavily staffed with professional personnel. Storage and transfer of raw materials are designed to handle interim experimental runs rather than routine operation, and the same comment applies to handling and packaging of finished product.

From the standpoint of consolidating a market position, however, either to service small orders for specialties or to stimulate advance demand for a new product, management may decide to operate pilot facilities as production units in spite of high costs. For specialty items it may be possible to set price scale to counteract the additional expense.

Process Engineering

The function of process engineering is to summarize all chemical and physical information from laboratory and process development experiments into a projected commercial operation, including preliminary economic estimates. This analysis should take into consideration the merits of changes in equipment and operating steps, substitution of alternative methodology, etc. Certain proposed modifications often need to be referred back to the laboratory or pilot plant for verification. Close cooperation between process engineers and research and development groups is necessary. Process engineering groups often carry out the functions defined as Techno-economic Evaluation.

The end product of process engineering is a flow diagram that shows the method recommended for carrying out commercial operation. It details quantities and specifications of raw materials; design, size, and construction materials for equipment; operating characteristics of equipment; instrumentation and controls; and materials and energy balances for the process.

Techno-economic Evaluation

Objective analysis of potential costs and profitability of a new venture is imperative, and such analyses should be made in varying degrees of depth of progressive stages. The analyses should include economic comparison with alternative processes which may be available. Determination of minimum economic size of plant may be required, as well as calculation of effect of varying size on cost. Techno-economic evaluations often include also estimates of sales volumes from the marketing department and estimated profitability.

Management is continually making economic judgments when it reaches decisions to continue or abandon a project. In all too many cases, these are opportunistic judgments based on opinions or subjective attitudes rather than on a comprehensive review of all pertinent variables.

Several points at which an economic review should be made to determine the future course of a project were indicated in the detailed list of steps and stages of product development in the preceding chapter. For example, after exploratory work has indicated some merit to an idea, a rough preliminary estimate of costs should be made. Such estimates can often be based on analogy to known operations, and experienced engineering evaluators build up sets of approximate factors for this purpose. A new chemical product might have, for example, a projected selling price of four times the yield-corrected raw material cost, based on commercial experience for related products; if it would be in a competitive field with materials selling at one-half this estimated price, its promise of success may be doubtful, unless it has special value to the user. Marketing experience reveals a psychological block to persuasion of a customer to pay twice the unit price for a product that is twice as efficient. From accumulated records and experience, these preliminary estimates of cost and capital investment become easier to make, but is must be kept in mind that they are suitable only as justification for decisions regarding research and development work, and not for firm calculation of cost and profit.

If further research continues to confirm the technical merits of a proposed product, the time will come when sufficient data are available to make a closer estimate. The process engineering group, from a sketch of initial design of plant, can reach a more reliable basis for decision to increase the scale of the project. Estimated costs of major items of equipment and use of factors for other elements of plant investment, plus a more detailed operating estimate from a flow sheet and manpower table, are needed.

The next step is the initial stage in detailed process engineering. A careful and complete plant lay-out should be prepared, and more accurate costs of major equipment items, piping, instruments, utilities, and the like, should be compiled. This should usually proceed in slightly delayed timing with the large-scale process development work, so that the results from the latter can serve as a basis for closer cost estimation.

The preceding discussion is directed to economic evaluation of major production units. Even for important modification and improvement of process or equipment, an appropriate depth of economic justification should be carried out.

Project Engineering

As stated at the beginning of the chapter, this engineering function is concerned with the planning, installation, and initial operation of large experimental units and commercial plant. It includes plant location; supervision of design, purchase, or fabrication of equipment; overseeing preparation of site, construction of buildings, and placement of equipment; and final testing and approval for operation. For large installations an outside engineering contractor is often used.

These responsibilities are best coordinated under a project engineer who is given general responsibility for overseeing the evolution of the operation from an intermediate development stage. In this way he acquires broad background in the technical considerations involved in final plans for the commercial plant. He supervises all detailed design, procurement, installation, and start-up. He is responsible for insuring that the equipment is installed according to specifications. Finally, he directs operation during the tune-in until it is functioning according to plan and responsibility is transferred to the manufacturing department.

CHAPTER **11**   COORDINATION
OF TECHNOLOGY
WITH MANUFACTURING

Quality Control

Cooperation of research and development with manufacturing to improve quality control methodology and implementation can be a very effective
avenue for enhancing the technologic posture of a company or an industry. This
subject has many implications, of which a few will be treated briefly.

Quality control in America is assuming greater importance in the eyes
of management. Although historically the function has been under the domination
of the manufacturing department, this is contrary to good management practices,
because self-policing of quality should not be the responsibility of the group responsible for managing the production operation. The question assumes new
importance in multi-plant manufacture of a nationally distributed item, for the
reputation and good will enjoyed by the company hinge on uniform standards of
quality. This is true also for products entering international trade. Hence in
such situations it has become more common to have a quality control coordinator,
reporting to a neutral member of general management, who is responsible for
establishment and dissemination of quality standards, summarizing and analyzing
data from different plants, and supervision of methods for enforcing specifications
throughout the company.

Proverbially, quality control has enjoyed little professional prestige,
because it involves repetitive use of standardized techniques which can be performed by employees with little or no technical training. Further, the results
are often not used constructively to improve operations, but only as a "go/no go"
means of rejecting substandard product. Introduction of sophisticated instrumentation requiring skill in operation and interpretation, use of statistical methods of analyzing results, and application of the findings in improving efficiency
of operation, are all forces toward greater recognition of the professional aspects of quality control programs.

As a means of familiarizing a scientist with the technologic problems
of an industry, participation in planning and implementing improved quality control has many advantages. Exposure to the procedures used in sampling and
evaluating raw materials, intermediate products, finished goods, and wastes
will give him first-hand knowledge of manufacturing difficulties and the quantitative relationships required by efficient management. Critical review of results often points out new technical problems susceptible to solution by research.
These can lead to important improvements in operations.

Quality Control Programs for Central Laboratories

In many older industries (e.g., food and textile products), quality has historically been judged by production supervisors on a basis which is largely subjective. This is true even in advanced economies.

Gradually, however, objective evaluation of quality is being introduced through internal laboratories or through a central technical group serving an industry. The steps involved in an industry association are usually taken in the following order: (1) The laboratory head, working with a representative cross-section of operating managers from different companies, prepares a list of the major quality problems. (2) From the literature and experimentation, the laboratory group develops suitable methods for evaluating samples for those quality factors deemed to be most important, with emphasis on those that simulate use by the customer. (3) A pilot study is then made in one or more plants for a practical procedure for collecting samples (which may include raw materials, intermediates, and finished products), analyzing them in the central laboratories, and reporting them in most useful form to the plants. (4) When a smooth system has been developed, the service is offered to all members of the industry. Those which accept the offer send in the specified samples on a regular basis (for example, once a month) and receive results on their own products, together with a summary of those of all participating plants.

This provides an entering wedge for the central laboratory to offer technical help to the industry as a whole. Gradually the program of quality control work is expanded, gradually research projects begin to take form, and as a result the whole industry moves forward to a higher level of technology. Many illustrative case histories of practical experiences of this type can be cited.

Use of Quality Control in Productivity Studies

Quality control results can be combined with quantitative data on flow of materials to improve yields, conservation of raw materials, and efficiency of operations. This subject is especially important in developing economies, because effective conversion of raw materials into finished product not only cuts down on wastes and the attendant increased cost per unit, but also decreases the overhead because of increased throughput.

A very useful purpose is therefore served by such "continuous materials balances" in which all materials are traced quantitatively through the process by analytical methods to determine the percentages of components that emerge as final product, rejects, by-products, or wastes. Similarly, an energy balance of the operation as a whole can lead to appreciable savings in fuel and power.

Technical Service to Manufacturing

Definition. This function comprises the use of technical information and know-how to assist the manufacturing department in current operations, including both efficiency of processing and maintenance of product quality. It does not include, as the term is generally used, work concerned with the introduction of new products or processes until they have become ready for routine operation; while they are being introduced, the required technical assistance is considered to be part of the development program.

Technical service problems are understood to be of short-range character. Any problems that need to be investigated in considerable depth are classified as research or development projects, and are referred to the research department if there is one or are set up in a special category in the technical service department.

Component Activities. In general, the problems may be described as "trouble shooting," and they can most easily be attacked by technical personnel who have close contact with day-to-day operations. In the chemical industry it is customary practice to have a plant laboratory, often closely coordinated with quality control, adequately staffed to do trouble shooting, in cooperation with supervisory production personnel and the plant engineering staff.

Many companies in industrialized countries maintain a policy of relying on the plant laboratory as the primary source of technical service to manufacturing on established processes and products; the research laboratory is not to be called on for extensive assistance until the production superintendent deems it necessary. This must not be construed as limiting normal interchange of technical information and cooperation between the two groups, which should be encouraged. It does mean, however, that all such important requests from the plant to the research laboratory should be cleared through appropriate channels. If the demands on the research laboratory for manufacturing service are high, it is often a sign that the production department is inadequately staffed with technical personnel. Work of this character is best accounted for through a service project, against which time and expense are collected for all requests for research laboratory assistance.

Maintenance Planning and Preventive Maintenance

The problem of maintaining continuity of manufacture by reducing the number and extent of operating break-downs is often of greater importance in a developing country than it might be under ordinary circumstances. Either an abnormally large stock of spare parts for all important items of equipment must be kept on hand, or the delay in fabricating a replacement part or in obtaining it from abroad must be faced. Even in mature economies, in which there are the facilities of many equipment manufacturers and spare part warehouses, the problems are regarded seriously.

For this reason there has been a trend toward a systematic mainte-nance policy to minimize accidental breakdowns and interruptions of production. Programs of this type involve three main types of activity: (1) historical review of break-down experience and orderly survey of working condition of plant equip-ment to provide a basis for forecasting the need for replacement parts; (2) peri-odic re-survey of all major machinery to up-date estimated life expectancy; and (3) judicious replacement at non-critical intervals, such as clean-up periods, of parts nearing exhaustion, in order to prevent their failure during a production run with consequent disruption of operating schedules.

Economic Balance in Selecting Process and Equipment

It is beyond the scope of this syllabus to devote more than passing mention to the quantitative relationships to be considered in making selections among alternative processes and machinery. There are many detailed articles and check lists in the specialized engineering literature dealing with the subject.

Economic analyses of this type are usually carried out by an engineer-ing group. Data are accumulated from all possible sources, such as the research laboratory, equipment suppliers, and other industrial users of equipment. These are then subjected to analysis in terms of initial cost, estimated production rate, utilization of labor, maintenance requirements, and capability of adjustment or expansion. The answer sought is the specification for the equipment which is best suited in over-all economics to meet the needs of the specific operation.

Many larger companies find it worthwhile to set up special laboratories for thorough evaluation of new types of equipment or for comparison of efficiency of two or more items performing similar functions. These laboratories may be under the direction of the central engineering group or the engineering develop-ment group, but both should be involved in planning and carrying out the tests.

Other Engineering Functions

It is beyond the scope of this syllabus to discuss such functions as plant design, industrial engineering, and conventional plant engineering.

CHAPTER 12

COORDINATION
OF TECHNOLOGY
WITH MARKETING

Technical Service to Marketing

Technical service to marketing consists of those activities classified
as short-range application research, sales service, preparation of special samples, and help to the production department in the solution of customer complaints
or problems, i.e., all those questions which require specialized effort beyond
the range of normal sales and manufacturing activities in order to create new
sales or retain existing business. Technical service to marketing does not include research on new products except where these are minor variations from
existing products ("new items" according to terminology used in this syllabus);
it does not include research on new or improved processes; it does not include
trouble shooting on routine processes for the manufacturing department.

Technical service has broader significance to a national economy than
merely the establishment of the desire of a customer to buy a given product. It
is actually a means of improving the technology of the consuming industries
themselves by placing in their hands products, equipment, or services that will
enable them to carry out their operations more effectively. This point is especially important in developing economies in which small enterprises have less
technical resourcefulness and therefore benefit more from assistance from companies supplying their starting materials.

Technical service to marketing is thus the use of technical information
and know-how to assist customers in using the products of the company. Normally the marketing department is the active party in furnishing readily available
information to individual purchasers in order that full benefit may be reaped in
the form of increased volume. Such information is in the form of brochures,
data sheets, and accumulated information in the files on the handling of related
inquiries. This is often supplemented by a staff of technical salesmen who serve
as field advisors to customers on use of the company's products. When these
are inadequate for answering a new question, technical service from the laboratory is required. Work of this category is short-range in nature and consists of
supplying information from the literature, from laboratory files, but particularly
from a limited amount of actual experimentation.

An important precaution to observe in handling technical service to the
sales staff is to clear all requests through one or more coordinating centers in
marketing management. Preferably there should be parallel coordination points
in the technical service group. If individual salesmen are allowed to ask directly
for help, control over the justification for requests is lost, and effort is dissipated

in haphazard fashion. Eventually the volume of work gets out of hand, and cor-
rective measures have to be taken. The coordination should not be so tightly
administered that necessary contact is shut off between the individuals in sales
and technical service who are directly involved, because cases always arise in
which additional explanation of the problem and review of the adequacy of the
answer are essential. Since speed of service is often a major factor in customer relations, undue delay in handling cases through formal channels should
be avoided.

Service to Marketing for Export Items and Consumer Products

The preceding section is addressed primarily to technical help in assisting industrial customers in the normal trading area to understand the properties, characteristics of use, and advantages of the products which the company
wishes to have them buy.

In international trade, there is increasing reliance on specifications
as a means of improving the basis for mutual agreement between buyer and seller,
who may never come into direct contact. Nations which wish to increase foreign
sales should encourage collection of information on formal specifications and informal trade standards of the markets to which they export, in order that these
may be interpreted by their manufacturing companies, which in turn may need
more technical help in meeting the requirements. As an example, food products
sold to industrialized countries have to meet certain trade standards of grading--
and sometimes legal standards of purity--to be acceptable in the market place.

Regarding technical service on consumer items, many of the larger
merchandising companies in the United States, including a number of department
stores, have installed laboratories, sometimes referred to as a "Bureau of
Standards," for evaluating the serviceability and economy of articles they sell to
the general public. The primary purpose is to enhance customer relations, but
there is an important secondary effect in the public interest, namely, continual
improvement in the value the customer receives for his money. This type of
technical service is, of course, in addition to technical work done by the manufacturers of the products. The merchandisers set specifications for fabrics and
clothing to ensure an optimum price-to-performance value for wear resistance,
washability, color fastness, etc. Similarly they study the durability and practicality of items of furniture and household equipment. There are also membership associations of consumers which evaluate commercial products on behalf of
their members. There are government agencies developing improved specifications in the interest of the general public.

Sample Preparation for the Trade

          In order to persuade an industrial customer to purchase a product, it
is often necessary to give him a trial sample so that he can make small-scale
tests to determine its usefulness in his operations. This is an activity which
needs to be controlled to a reasonable level, because there is always a danger
that the cost of the service in individual cases will greatly outweigh the potential
benefit to the enterprise. Excessive demands by marketing can be counteracted
by charging the expense of technical service to cost of sales. There are numerous justifiable occasions, however, when a customer or prospect desires a
minor variation in specification for a special purpose. On the other hand, the
provision of samples of new products should be considered part of the appropriate
individual research projects, and this activity is assigned to the research laboratory when there is one, rather than to technical service to marketing.

          A destructive dilution of technical effort can result from excessive
requests for submission of samples of new products for which it has not been
determined that they can be economically produced. Such requests may have
value as new product ideas, but if they are considered in this light they should
be subjected to the usual screening procedures employed for research suggestions. Furthermore, unless experimental samples are clearly identified as
laboratory products, the user has a right to feel injured if he bases his new
product thereon, only to learn subsequently that the material is not the same as
that which becomes commercially available. The moral is that the sample should
resemble as closely as possible in raw material and final specifications the product which is anticipated from commercial production.

Determination of Properties

          This form of technical service to marketing arises when a customer
needs information on physical, chemical, or performance properties not included in the company literature and product specifications. However, where
new products undergo end-use testing designed to determine their suitability for
given applications, such determination of properties may be more logically considered application research.

Application Research

          This encompasses a wide range of technical activity ranging from
routine end-use testing to determine suitability of product, to detailed screening
of new products to evaluate performance in a number of end uses, including the
development of variations of existing products and comparison of their properties

for specific purposes. Much of the product development program of the research laboratory is actually application research. The more routine forms of application research may be handled to better advantage by the technical service group or by the plant laboratory without recourse to the research laboratory.

Complaints

Customer complaints may involve dissatisfaction with product quality, packaging, delivery, or invoicing (price and terms). Only when the customer complaints involve quality are they considered to be in the domain of technical service to sales. Fast, efficient, and considerate handling of complaints is a powerful marketing tool which often results in a better customer relationship than existed before. Further, analysis of the composite complaint record frequently leads to desirable improvements in product.

Analysis of Competition

No marketing program can be considered to be truly sophisticated unless it is based on awareness of the products the company faces competitively in the market place. And competition must be interpreted broadly, as involving not only products made by other enterprises within the industry, but also those from other industries which serve a similar function, a situation that is often termed "inter-industry competition." As an illustration, a manufacturer of pottery jars for food products may make the best jars in the pottery industry, but he may be losing his market to tin cans, glass bottles, paper packages, or plastic pouches.

Technical assistance to marketing vis-à-vis competition involves: (1) collection of commercial samples of product from leading manufacturers under comparable conditions; (2) carrying out systematic evaluation of the chemical, physical, or use properties on all samples; and (3) scoring comparative performance of the samples from all sources by a uniform system. In passing, it may be mentioned that cases are by no means unknown in which manufacturers of semi-perishable or perishable products have fooled themselves by comparing their own samples taken directly from production lines against competitive samples secured after exposure to the rigors of the open market.

Turning to the problem of evaluating products against competition in export markets, there are many examples of companies in industrialized countries which have had unfortunate experiences in trying to market products in foreign countries without taking into account the established consumer appeal of competitors' products already available there. While circumstances make it

more difficult to carry out comparisons abroad, if the goal is important enough
to warrant the effort, trade intelligence channels can be established to pick up
the necessary information and competitive samples.

Market Research

This activity is concerned with the study of the sales potential of new
items, new products, or new product lines, or with major new uses for present
products. It should be distinguished from sales analysis, which is the systematic
study of market records of existing products.

Market research has become a specialized function which is well
recognized for its value in the United States, where strong competition from
numerous suppliers in a very large national market has encouraged systematic
investigation of sales opportunities for innovative products. The function has,
generally speaking, been less highly developed in Western Europe, but in recent
years there has been much more interest in, and adoption of, the techniques.
The evolution of large economic complexes (ECM and FTA) and opportunities for
greater penetration of international markets have encouraged the trend.

In brief, market research employs a combination of business and
technical information in a systematic analysis of market opportunities. The
function has been highly developed in the chemical industry, for example, and
there are now two professional organizations (Chemical Market Research Association and Commercial Chemical Development Association), with several
hundred members in each, which through their meetings provide a forum for
discussion of common problems of methodology.

As an illustration of market research techniques, a systematic screening procedure is first established to define market areas which should be of potential interest to the company. The end result will be sets of tabulations of raw
materials, intermediates, end products, products by specific application, and
products by consuming industry. These should be rated by a simple scoring
system (e.g., "high," "medium," "low") according to appropriate industry
criteria (e.g., growth rate, future profitability, size of investment required,
and character of technology). A separate rating of the product areas in terms
of the strengths and weaknesses of the company gives a second set of criteria
describing the degree of fit to corporate objectives, technologic strengths, and
marketing capability. Systematic study of the tables permits selection of a number of areas which show a promising outlook by industry criteria and which also
conform to the company's development potential. A second screening with more
selective criteria (such as growth rate, return on investment, magnitude of investment, level of research effort, character of operating technology, technical

service requirements, marketing complexity, cyclicality or seasonality, and restrictive factors such as patents or entrenched competition) facilitates narrowing the list of attractive possibilities for immediate evaluation.

Once the market areas for investigation have been selected, the detailed investigation begins. Information is collected on needs of customers for new or improved products or services, the volumes that might be sold, prices and volumes of existing products that are being used for related purposes, and the price range that would be acceptable to customers for products meeting new performance specifications. This may be done for a product in process of development, or on a longer-range basis for identifying the needs that innovative new products should satisfy.

One might superficially assume that an approach of this sort is not suited to the situation in a developing economy. Admittedly, the methodology described above appears very complicated, but the principles have been, and are being, used by larger enterprises and government planning agencies in less highly industrialized countries. The subject is brought up here to emphasize the view that this sort of analysis should be more widely used to permit appropriate channeling of technical effort in the most promising directions.

Consumer Research

This function is the specialized search into consumer needs and wants to determine practical methods of satisfying them. Manufacturers of products sold to retail markets have developed a range of techniques for determining the preferences of representative panels as a means of forecasting those of the buying public as a whole. A good specific example is the "Sensory Testing Guide for Panel Evaluation of Foods and Beverages" recently prepared by a committee of the Institute of Food Technologists. Commercial introduction of new consumer products is often made through test markets in a few selected centers; the results of these pilot sales tests form the basis for decision regarding the launching of the product on a broader scale.

Rationale of Project Systems

Experience has convinced a great many directors of research and development that a greater degree of formality needs to be introduced into planning and controlling the segments of the technical program. They find that opportunistic policies of permitting work to expand haphazardly in a technical area initially thought to be attractive, without reference to defined objectives, usually results in considerable expenditure of effort in unproductive directions. Lack of a framework for comparison of one area of investigation against another with respect to probable benefits leads to project administration characterized by subjective reactions rather than objective analysis.

Therefore, systems of formal projects have been widely used, and the application of this planning technique is expanding. While details vary considerably among different laboratories, the general principle is to define an objective with a level of specificity suitable to the type of work, and to estimate the allocation of manpower--and preferably the cost of the work--needed to meet the goal. Obviously long-range research requires a broad definition of scope, while a phase of development close to commercialization can be specified quite narrowly.

If a project system is to be effective, it should be carried out with firm adherence to established criteria for evaluating effort versus benefit. It is not sufficient to write up project outlines, go through the motions of periodic review and revision, and then fail to make and enforce meaningful decisions about the future course of the individual lines of research. Lackadaisical administration can easily reduce a system to unproductive discussions and paper work.

Project Outlines

The type of project outline most generally used includes the items listed below. The selected project leader should be given responsibility for preparing the outline.

1. A brief descriptive title and serial number;

2. A concise statement of the objective or goal of the work (stepwise phases or stages are a preferred procedure, with the initial project outline confined to the given phase, but mention is often made of the phases that are likely to follow);

3. An estimate of the value of the work to the company in terms of potential new business and profit, savings in manufacturing costs from improved processes, etc.;

4. A brief outline of the proposed plan of work;

5. An estimate of duration, amount of effort (preferably in the form of a budget), and any capital expenditures for equipment required to carry out the program;

6. Designation of the project leader, and estimate of the type and number of personnel to be involved in the work; and

7. Authorization by signature from the proper executives.

Estimation of the potential value of a long-range project of course presents difficulties. Nevertheless, a serious attempt should be made to evaluate the probable impact of the work on the business of the company in as definite a manner as is appropriate to the subject.

A sample project outline is shown in Figure 6.

Minor Assignments

Most laboratories find it a nuisance to go through these detailed procedures for small, short-term projects, because the amount of time involved in preparing outlines and securing approval is out of proportion to the effort involved in carrying them out. Experience has shown that these minor assignments can be effectively administered by means of a few comprehensive or omnibus projects. Such categories of work need to be carefully policed to prevent misuse. In each case there should be a project outline describing the types of work to be included and an estimate of the amount of time and expense to be devoted during the budget period, normally one year, for all individual assignments falling into the classification.

Preliminary exploratory work on proposed ideas is often lumped under such a project. A reasonable figure for the amount of work of this type to be conducted during a one-year period would be in the neighborhood of 10 percent of the total technical time of the laboratory; the charges against the project will probably vary considerably among individuals, groups and periods within the budget year, depending on number of ideas, workload, etc.

No. _____

Group or
Section _____

Date _____

Subject _____

Object _____

Value to Enterprise (include brief summary of economic and market justification)

_____
_____
_____
_____
_____

Plan of Investigation _____

_____
_____
_____
_____
_____
_____
_____
_____

Completion Date _____

Cost _____ Special Capital Expense _____

Project Leader _____ Reporting Schedule _____

Personnel Requirements _____

If this is a continuation of a previous project, give the following information:

Date of Original Project _____

Total Sum Spent in Previous Periods _____

Authorization
Date of Endorsement by Research Committee _____
Approved by Technical Executive

_____   _____
Signature   Date

Approved by Management Executive

_____   _____
Signature   Date

FIGURE 6   PROJECT OUTLINE

Other comprehensive projects are often set up to collect miscellaneous small items of technical service, for instance under the titles Technical Service to Sales, Technical Service to Manufacturing, etc.

All projects of this type should be limited to individual items not involving more than the equivalent of, for example, one-half of one man-month of technical time, without special authorization from the appropriate laboratory supervisor. A numbered list of assignments should be kept under each comprehensive project, together with estimated and actual effort and expense. Close watch should be kept to convert the individual items into regular projects as soon as the results and magnitude of future work justify such an assignment.

Continuing Projects

"Continuing" projects, going on from year to year, present a hazard in that effort may be devoted to them over a long period without critical analysis of their justification in the light of changes in conditions which have developed since they were started. Although work over a period of years may be warranted, it is recommended that at each annual review period a revised project outline should be prepared for the next year. The same project number may be retained for filing or charging purposes, but there should be a thoroughgoing analysis of project effort against anticipated benefits.

Overhead Projects

Many organizations feel it is worthwhile to account for time spent in activities other than those directly connected with technical programs. They often set up project outlines to cover the following subjects:

General administration, usually limited to time
   charges of supervisory personnel;

Personnel, including recruiting, performance reviews,
   salary and wage administration;

Professional activities, such as attendance at meetings
   and preparation of papers;

Vacation, illness.

Technical executives who institute overhead project control are often surprised at the percentage of time of personnel consumed in these necessary

but indirect allocations. They will usually account for a total of 25-30 percent
of available man-hours. Analysis of performance will often yield information
leading to better administrative practices to obtain higher input into direct
activities.

It is desirable to keep the number of overhead projects low, because
it is unlikely that minute details of the time charges will serve a useful purpose.
If a special check on some activity appears warranted, this can be done through
an interim collection of data in order to determine whether a new project is required to control expenditure of effort.

Review of Program

As a general example of the information a project system can bring to
light, the following make-up of a program is typical of distribution of effort that
might be encountered in a laboratory.

	Percentage of Total Time of Personnel
Overhead Projects	25
Exploratory Work	10
Long-term research	10
Intermediate-range projects	15
Short-term projects	25
Technical service to manufacturing	5
Technical service to marketing	10

Is this optimum use of the company's technical resources? It is necessary to analyze the individual projects of each of these major classes in order to
establish a sound basis for change in emphasis among them. Obviously the questions cited below cannot be answered from the gross percentages but require detailed review of the technical content of the component assignments. Are the
overhead accounts in realistic proportion to the needs of the organization? Is
time spent on exploratory experiments being inflated by permitting lines of work
to continue too long before defining specific projects? Is the allocation to long-
term research in balance with the plans of the company for expansion into new
areas? Are there continuing intermediate-range studies being conducted which
have diminished in importance since they were first started? Does the list of
short-term projects contain many which are really technical service? Should the

manufacturing department increase its technical strength to handle more problems internally? Is the sales department asking for more help than seems
justified for servicing minor trade inquiries?

Periodic review of the entire list of projects on a regular basis, say
quarterly or semi-annually, should be made in order to re-evaluate progress,
objectives, and priorities within the over-all program. Revisions in the estimated target dates and amount of effort and expense of individual lines of work
are to be expected because of results obtained in the interim. Management should
recognize the need for flexibility in project programs resulting from such periodic revisions, because this procedure encourages a realistic appraisal of how
the talents of the technical department can best be used in the interest of the
company.

Project Assignments

The project leadership and project team composition should be established on the basis of the requirements of each task and the available technical
talents within the staff. These assignments should be subject to shift during the
course of the work as judgment indicates. For example, a project to develop a
new product will probably involve, as a first phase, a minor task (under the
comprehensive exploratory project) for an evaluation program to determine the
merits of the proposal. If the evaluation work is favorable, one of the senior
men will be placed in charge of a regular project with the usual project outline
form being used for this phase. If the results of the laboratory investigations
are successful, the project will be turned over to a development engineer who
will have charge of working out the process. The leadership might then be
turned over to a member of the marketing research staff who would be responsible for the necessary internal evaluation of commercial potential. Finally, the
responsibility for working out production equipment and procedures would be
turned over to the appropriate plant engineering personnel. Each of these assignments might be covered as a separate project, or alternatively they might
be covered as phases of one major project. In the next chapter, more detailed
procedures for technical task force operation are described.

Procedures for Installing Project Systems

Experience shows the wisdom of starting the operation of a project
system gradually. Attempts to convert abruptly from conventional procedures
in which the supervisors control the program without projects usually result in
much confusion and frustration. Major complaints from the staff center around
the difficulty of segregating a segment of work from other interlocking activities,

the inability to foresee the amount of effort required to reach the goal, and the inaccuracies and nuisance of keeping records of time expenditure. All these objections are gradually overcome by experience of the staff with the system through on-the-job indoctrination, particularly if reasonable tolerance is shown by supervisors in dealing with deficiencies in preparation of project outlines, inaccuracies in estimates of manpower requirements and completion dates, and inconsistencies in records of time expenditure, until the personnel have attained proficiency through practice.

The wise course to follow is to select one or more tasks of considerable importance and size as illustrative examples. The staff members involved in them can be brought to see why it is important to have a definite plan for the work. In practice they learn that there is flexibility enough to take care of faulty estimates and that the burden of keeping records is by no means so heavy as they at first feared.

Budgeting Control Procedures

For a project system to be truly effective, some measure of technical input by individual staff members is necessary. This should be of suitable simplicity to reduce paper work, but adequate to provide information to team leaders speedily. It need not be directly tied to the formal accounting procedures, although ingenuity will usually reveal an appropriate means of so doing.

Two advantages accrue from such accounting: (1) it provides a basis for judging the amount of effort that is warranted on a given project in relation to estimated financial benefits from its success; (2) it makes all personnel cost-conscious and helps to sharpen their individual evaluations of the directions in which their efforts can best be spent.

Various types of controls are used in different organizations. As a beginning step, many companies institute a weekly report of number of hours spent by professional (and often non-professional technical) personnel on various projects. Each project leader is given the breakdown of hours spent by different individuals on his project during the week, for comparison with his man-hour estimate. Unfortunately, one sees a number of cases in which such information is collected regularly but is not used as a managerial tool.

The next step in refinement is to apply an average figure for technical-man-hour cost (which should include all direct and indirect items) to apply to the total number of man-hours spent on each project. This has the advantage of giving a monetary figure, but it does not distinguish between more costly professionals of high skill and their junior colleagues and non-professional technicians.

Finally, the system reaches maximum usefulness when the man-hours expended are translated into true costs, either on the basis of marked-up actual salaries (which may necessitate special accounting precautions against disclosure of individual salaries) or on progressive class rates for different salary groupings. These hourly figures in either case should of course include the full overheads. The method found most satisfactory in many organizations is to give each project leader a weekly list of hours spent by each team member and the total of the time costs incurred.

The usual time interval in such reporting systems is one man-hour, but successful systems are operating on a quarter-hour basis. The accuracy of time reporting depends on the individual, of course, but persistent indoctrination leads to reasonable data for managerial purposes.

Some organizations require detailed charging of apparatus and supplies against projects. Except for unusually large exepnditures, such as for expensive equipment, it is doubtful that this detail is worth the effort during laboratory stages. The total of salaries, wages, and fringe benefits in most laboratories will be in the neighborhood of two-thirds of operating budget. Further, emphasis on minutiae obscures the basic purpose of a project system, which is to make optimum use of the major resource, namely, technical abilities.

CHAPTER **14** TECHNICAL
TASK FORCES

Multi-Discipline Approach

Task forces or project teams, made up of individuals with diversified backgrounds and experience, are being used increasingly in American industry to expedite solution of major technical problems. Their effectiveness is noteworthy in accelerating the movement of projects from inception to commercialization.

A task force system involves: (1) setting up for each major project an outline with stated goal, justification, plan of attack, target date, and cost estimate as discussed in the preceding chapter; (2) appointing a team leader with responsibility for organizing and managing the diversified group of specialists needed for his assignment. Team membership very frequently crosses formal organization lines. The members often take part in a given project on a flexible, part-time basis, which is controlled by the project leader to secure optimum input of specialized skills and knowledge. The balance of their time is allocated among other projects and duties.

The benefits from a task force system are a matter of established experience and not just wishful thinking. All work at Arthur D. Little, Inc., is carried out in this manner, with a total of about 700 professional employees engaged at any one time on several hundred separate assignments for clients. These same operating procedures are being adopted to an increasing extent by industrial organizations.

Advantages of Task Force Systems

Attack on problems by project teams emphasizes FEED-IN of specialized information with optimum timing, as opposed to the circuitous FEED-BACK, which is inherent in the routine operation of a formal organization.

To be more specific, the advantages of task force operation are:

1. The varied professional skills and know-how required to reach an optimum solution of a problem are brought to bear with appropriate timing and emphasis.

2. Speed-up in development stages and commercial implementation is brought about through concurrent FEED-IN of needed information and opinion from all parts of the company, rather than through reliance on the more round-about functioning of formal organization channels which results in time lag between formulation of comments and consideration by the responsible individuals.

3. Obstacles to success of a problem are brought to light at earlier stages, thus speeding up decisions to discontinue or modify programs, thereby saving unproductive effort.

4. The mechanics of the system provide for effective transfer of background and know-how from step to step.

5. Acceptance of the project and preparation for implementation are promoted among operating departments and staff groups by enlisting their participation in earlier stages.

6. Empire-building tendencies in individual departments are reduced by making available a pool of talents from elsewhere in the company organization.

7. More effective mobilization of technical manpower is achieved as a result of inherent pressures of the system on those responsible for deploying personnel resources.

8. Morale and professional development of technical personnel are stimulated by giving them wide scope in range of activities and a greater sense of responsibility for projects in which they are involved.

9. A task force system leads to a flatter technical organization, i.e., a structure with fewer administrative echelons, thus promoting more effective use of available professional skills in project work.

10. A positive thrust is provided toward knitting together the component sections of the organization by uniting their joint efforts in carrying projects forward from inception to commercialization.

Illustrative Case History of Task Force Operation

The manner in which a task force operates can best be illustrated by a specific case. This example is purposely fairly complex in order to make clear the procedures involved.

Exploratory work by a technologist in Product Development, based on a discovery in Applied Research, has aroused interest in a new idea for a nutritious breakfast food which may have special appeal because of unusual form and convenience. Preliminary discussions with Market Research and Sales have indicated that they are receptive to a product of this type. Enough exploration is carried out to collect information in sufficient depth about composition, raw materials, processing, consumer appeal, and potential market to warrant establishment of a project.

The originator of the idea, one of the senior men in Product Development, is authorized to prepare a project proposal describing objective, plan of attack, amount of technical effort, cost of this effort, and the target date for completion of the assignment up to semi-commercial production and market test. The project is approved and the task force authorized (see Table 5).

TABLE 5

TASK FORCE FOR NEW BREAKFAST FOOD

Skill	Percentage of Working Time					
	Jan.	Feb.	Mar.	Apr.	May	June
Project Leader, Food Technologist	30	30	30	30	40	50
Product Development Technologist	30	30	40	40	40	40
Junior Product Development Technologist	50	50	50	60	60	75
Home Economics Specialist	15	15	15	15	15	15
Physical Chemist	5	5	5	10	10	10
Carbohydrate Chemist	20	20	10	10	5	5
Protein Chemist	10	10	10	5	5	5
Nutrition Chemist	5	5	-	-	5	5
Analytical Specialist	-	-	10	20	20	20
Process Engineer	5	5	10	10	20	25
Market Research Specialist	10	10	15	15	20	20

The project leader does not have formal administrative control over any of the individuals in the task force. In a large organization, it is probable that only he and the other two food technologists would be in the laboratory section designated as Product Development. The four chemists might well be located in science groups in Applied Research. The Home Economics Expert and the Analytical Specialist are responsible for functions frequently included in a Laboratory Services section. The Process Engineer could be a representative from a separate Engineering Development Department. The Market Research Specialist might report administratively to Marketing, Corporate Development, or the Technical Director's staff, depending on the organization in the particular company.

The project leader's estimate of technical input, which was the basis for preliminary estimates of cost and timing, includes about one-third of his own time for six months. He foresees need for the pattern of technical skills in Table 5 in order to give a well-rounded answer to his assignment. He clears informally with the selected individuals and with those to whom they report administratively (group heads or section supervisors) to confirm their interest and availability for the project. When the work has been authorized, he formalizes arrangements for this participation, including approximate amounts of time, work assignments, reporting procedures, and the like. The amount of time and subject matter required from each person cannot be defined rigidly, because the project leader must use his judgment of desirable technical input as the work progresses. Not shown in Table 5 or in the subsequent coordination chart (Figure 7) is a special group which may be called upon for evaluating the product from the consumer's point of view.

By virtue of the approval of the project and the agreement with the individuals and their line supervisors, however, all these specialists have been placed under the project leader's technical jurisdiction for the purpose of this particular project. Each has the rest of his working time allocated to other task forces and duties, and in the former may sometimes act as team leader, sometimes as participant or consultant. If major difficulties should arise between the team leader and one of the members regarding the performance of the latter, the team leader has the option of relieving him of project responsibility or carrying the matter to his administrative superior. However, voluntary service on the team because of interest in the project is a major premise of the system, and enforcement of participation by disciplinary action is highly undesirable. Tactful replacement of the offender and reallocation of his duties is the wise solution in such cases, which fortunately are rare. When they do occur, there is usually an acceptable explanation, such as unexpected pressure from other responsibilities, so that readjustment of team membership can be brought about amicably.

It is highly unlikely that the initial plan for manpower will fit exactly the actual requirements for input of technical skills. Hence there must be enough flexibility in the administration of the project system as a whole to deploy fruitfully the total personnel resources among the array of projects and staff activities. This calls for executive ability to ensure optimum distribution of workload.

If all goes well and the project leader has been a good manager, the various component sub-tasks in his scheme will have been properly carried out and interlocked so that he can make a report on his assigned responsibility on the target date and within the budget.

If executive review of the findings and recommendations of this task force is favorable, the project will move into the next phases--normally pilot manufacture and field tests of market potential. The members of the initial task force will then have their available time distributed to other activities. To ensure continuity in the transfer of knowledge and background, the leader of the development project and other selected members of the product development team will be asked to participate in the new phases.

Corporate Coordination of Task Forces

The preceding section is concerned with the organization of a product development task force. If the full benefits of this method of operation are to be realized, this unit must be treated as an organic part of the corporate structure set-up to carry the project through to commercial stage. As it and its successor project teams move toward their goals, with over-all guidance from project overseers, the knowledge of their progress should be integrated into company planning and programming, from Management objectives to preparatory steps by Manufacturing and Marketing.

Figure 7 illustrates schematically a general procedure for bringing about corporate coordination. Only incidental reference is made to the development and commercialization of a new breakfast food used as an example in the preceding section, but if this project is kept in mind, it will provide a background of practicality against which the discussion can be interpreted.

To codify the coordinative relationships, it is helpful to define four types of participation in the planning, conduct, evaluation, and implementation of task force activities. These are the following, which are discussed below under these headings:

1. Team Leadership,

2. Team Participation,

3. Consultative Responsibility,

4. Information Requirement.

Team Leadership - The functions of the team leader have been defined as planning the project, organizing the required team, managing the input of technical skills, and summarizing results of the work in suitable form for decision as to future course of action.

Team Participation - The bulk of the work on a given project will usually, but not necessarily, be performed in the administrative group within which the team leader is located. This relationship makes readily apparent his direct authority, transmitted to him by the section supervisor, to plan and supervise the activities of his co-workers insofar as these lie within the scope of the task force. Those participants in other administrative groups, although there is no formal channel of authority to the team leader, are technically responsible to him for the performance of the duties they have agreed (with concurrence of their supervisors) to perform. In other words, administratively they remain responsible to their line supervisors for general overseeing of their activities, but, within the provisions of assignments to specific project teams, their technical participation is under the control of the respective team leaders.

Consultative Responsibility - In this capacity, participants are called on for comment and criticism, rather than for detailed work. Their function is to keep generally informed of the progress of the project, and to interject comments at suitable intervals on the basis of their specialized backgrounds. To illustrate the point, in the case of the breakfast food, the relationships of the Process Engineer and Market Researcher might be considered as consultative rather than participative during the product development stage, particularly in its early phase. The Process Engineer has the responsibility of outlining the requirements for large-scale operation to guide laboratory or pre-pilot work in such matters as process feasibility, equipment characteristics, and preliminary estimates of plant investment and operating cost. The Market Researcher should feed in his opinions as to pertinent criteria for marketing, such as product specifications and quality, packaging, shelf life, competitive trends, distribution channels, and the like.

Information Requirement - This fourth type of involvement may be described as a watch-dog responsibility. These participants should be suitably informed, without overburdening them in details, of the course of the project, so that they can raise questions or warnings that must be taken into consideration. This does not imply formal approval, the procedures for which would slow up the work, but places on them the responsibility of speaking up on critical matters. Top Management, for example, has of course the prerogative of stepping in at any time to raise issues, but at certain critical stages should be specifically informed, in order to review project status in terms of corporate goals and criteria for new products. The Purchasing Department should point out problems concerned with raw material supply. Finally, at later stages the key participants in earlier phases should be kept informed, so that they can feed in any new information acquired since they were directly involved.

Coordination Chart - Figure 7, condensed from a detailed check list of stages and steps in product development such as that given in an earlier chapter, illustrates the principles of coordination for a hypothetical case in a hypothetical organization. It indicates by code the pattern of Team Leadership, Team Participation, Consultative Responsibility, and Information Requirement at individual steps in major phases of product development. To reduce detail, it has been aimed at action steps and in general omits the procedures for executive and committee approval at intermediate stages; for example, consideration of any sizable investment in pilot plant would properly go to management for review and decision.

In a given corporate structure, obviously the degree of involvement of different departments will vary according to type of project, qualifications of individuals involved, and the prescribed procedures of operation. The spread of functions across the top of Figure 7 is representative of those likely to be found in a large company. Without dwelling on the possible range of variations from this idealized chart, it is obvious that circumstances will justify considerable modification.

While Figure 7 shows the steps in sequential order, obviously it will be advantageous in many major programs to have some of them running concurrently. Because of overlapping membership in the component teams, transfer of essential information from one phase to another can take place smoothly. An important function of a project overseer, defined below, as coordinator of all phases, is to make sure that the individual steps are undertaken with appropriate timing and level of work.

Project Overseership - To insure effectiveness in transfer from stage to stage, some person of adequate administrative status should be appointed as an expediter to have over-all responsibility for moving the project ahead. This individual may be one of the team leaders, provided that he has the necessary competence, breadth, force, and authority. He must be given power to make decisions and to demand action. In a project of highest priority, it may be appropriate to assign this over-all responsibility to a member of top management. To avoid further complicating the chart, the functions of the Project Overseer have been omitted from Figure 7.

How to Introduce Task Force Operations

The use of task forces represents a profound change from operation on the basis of a formal organization. For those who are habituated to the latter system, the complexities involved in shifting to the great flexibility of project teams will cause some confusion. A man will frequently ask: "How can I possibly

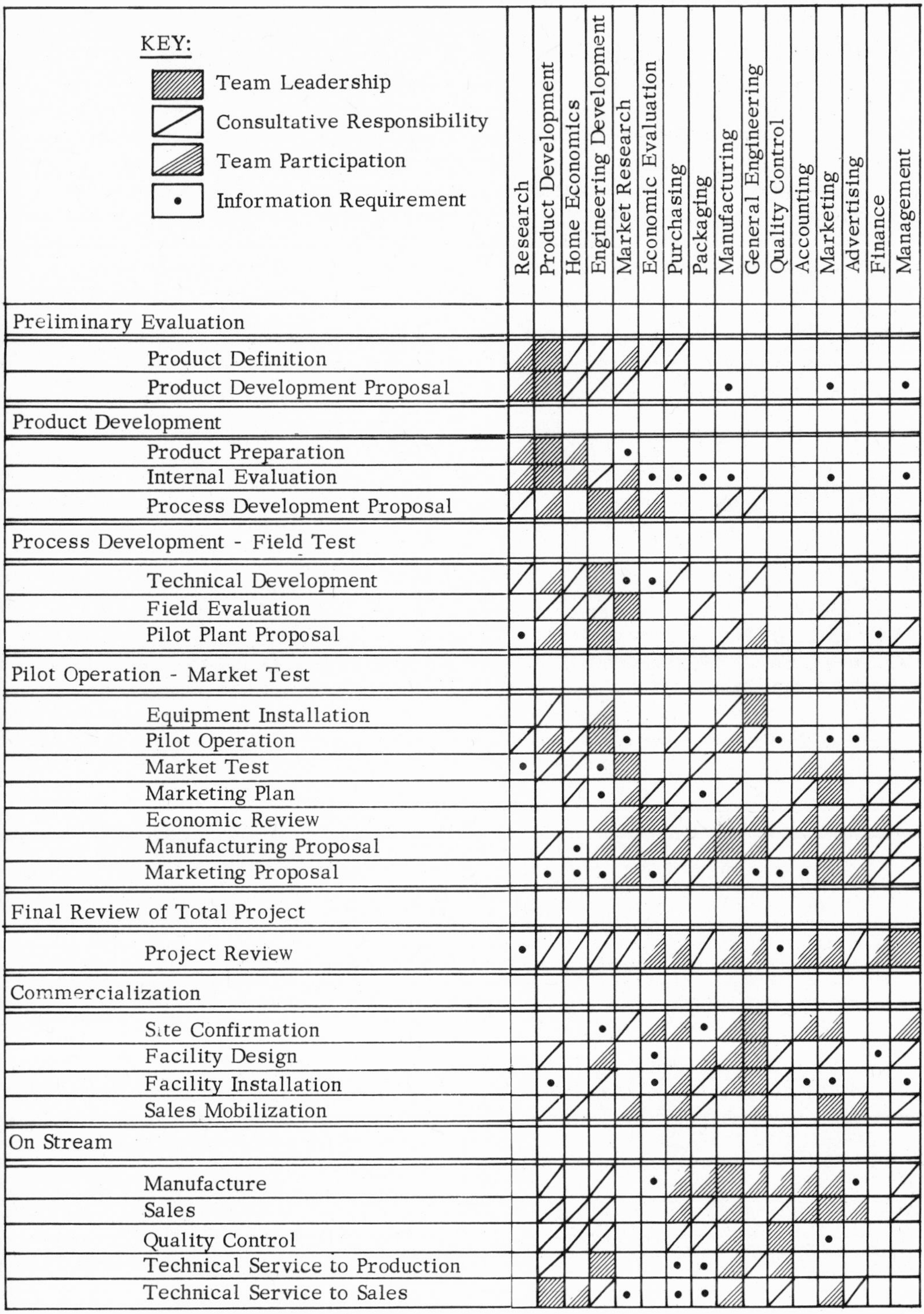

KEY:

- ▨ Team Leadership
- ◩ Consultative Responsibility
- ▨ Team Participation
- • Information Requirement

Column headers:
Research | Product Development | Home Economics | Engineering Development | Market Research | Economic Evaluation | Purchasing | Packaging | Manufacturing | General Engineering | Quality Control | Accounting | Marketing | Advertising | Finance | Management

Preliminary Evaluation

- Product Definition
- Product Development Proposal

Product Development

- Product Preparation
- Internal Evaluation
- Process Development Proposal

Process Development - Field Test

- Technical Development
- Field Evaluation
- Pilot Plant Proposal

Pilot Operation - Market Test

- Equipment Installation
- Pilot Operation
- Market Test
- Marketing Plan
- Economic Review
- Manufacturing Proposal
- Marketing Proposal

Final Review of Total Project

- Project Review

Commercialization

- Site Confirmation
- Facility Design
- Facility Installation
- Sales Mobilization

On Stream

- Manufacture
- Sales
- Quality Control
- Technical Service to Production
- Technical Service to Sales

FIGURE 7   PROJECT COORDINATION CHART

report administratively to a superior and yet spend most of my time working professionally under others who are not in the direct chain of command?" Rather than to attempt to answer this question at length, it should suffice to say that a great many professional men find that, once the ground rules are understood, they experience an even more exciting challenge in the greater latitude of task force philosophy of matching skills against needs.

Another question frequently asked is: "How do task forces differ from committees?" A task force is indeed a type of committe in the broad denotation of the word. On the other hand, by connotation a committee acts as a deliberative body, reaching consensus on the basis of information assembled on its behalf. A task force is an action group which generates and correlates its own information, often for submission to a committee, which then reaches decision from the facts and opinions placed before it.

For important, complex projects, which have lost impetus for one reason or another, many companies will use task forces to speed up coordination of the loose ends for final review and decision. In such cases the management has recognized the inherent strength of a project team operation to meet a situation of emergency. This device, however, has meant a departure from the normal method of operation in those organizations which adhere to the formal pattern. After the particular problem has been solved, inertia is likely to restore status quo until the next emergency arises.

These considerations, therefore, lead to the belief that any change to task forces from operation under formal organization should be brought about gradually. By selecting a few good cases and, through sympathetic supervision, guiding project teams into smooth operation, one can make apparent not only the advantages of this managerial technique, but also the fact that the individual can thrive under the stimulus. Task forces can then be gradually adopted more widely until they become the major organizational pattern.

It should be remembered that there will be work which can best be conducted by an individual and his assistants rather than through an organized project. This is especially true of exploratory types of work in which the creativity of a single scientist is needed. The experience of serving on task forces on formal projects, however, will probably predispose him to make greater use of the talents of other people.

In advanced defense technology, because of the complexities in dealing with major problems in system capabilities, procedures have been evolved for the use of "critical path methods" (CPM) and "program evaluation and review techniques" (PERT). By segregating the planning and scheduling phases and subjecting the isolated variables to analysis by probability theory, an important tool is being forged for logical treatment of development programs. The problems in industry relating to product development may appear superficially to require no such abstract dissection of methodology, but actually there is already considerable use in some sophisticated sectors. It is safe to forecast that CPM, PERT, and their relatives and offspring will come into general use as an aid to the management of industrial projects.

CHAPTER 15

COORDINATION
OF CORPORATE
DEVELOPMENT FUNCTIONS

<u>Corporate Planning</u>

There is a distinct trend among companies in industrialized countries
to adopt systematic long-range planning as a means of projecting policies and
programs of the firm toward a successful future. This is a manifestation of
acceptance of the "doctrine of progressive change" as a basic business philosophy.

The functions involved are frequently described collectively as
"corporate development" or "corporate planning." These functions are in
practice often assigned to a small staff group reporting to the chief executive.
The influence of these activities extends broadly throughout all the operations
of the company, but we are chiefly concerned here with the guidance that is af-
forded to the technical departments.

Some conservative executives resist the idea of planning functions
because of fear that they will interfere with their responsibility and authority
for making decisions. This view is a fallacy. Planning does not infringe the
prerogatives of managerial decision, but, on the contrary, it aids the process
by providing documentation of the probable results of alternative courses of
action.

In a later section in this chapter appears a set of definitions of the
functions usually included in a corporate development program in American
companies. It should be understood that a department established to spear-head
the activity can be quite small in size, and that experience shows the merits of
a policy of conducting its studies and formulating its recommendations to management by means of task forces selected largely from the rest of the organization. In fact, the first steps toward corporate planning can be carried out effectively on a part-time basis by a qualified individual. As the program demonstrates its value, this can be made a full-time assignment for him, and later a
small staff of specialists can be assembled.

By way of illustration of planning philosophy, it is by no means unique
to hear a company president say that he has definite corporate objectives, namely,
to see that the enterprise returns higher profits and increases its sales. It is
obvious that such generalizations provide no basis for defining technical programs,
or, in fact, for inspiring any other type of orderly analysis of business opportunities.

The framing of corporate objectives and criteria for evaluation of projects in terms of these objectives is a feasible undertaking. From our experience,

the first hurdle is a commitment by management to make an earnest attempt to develop planning procedures. Then some competent individual must be given the initial assignment of reducing to writing the general policies for future growth. This activity is aided by a survey of strengths and weaknesses in the present pos- ture of the enterprise, as described in an earlier chapter. From such a survey certain objectives can be set forth as a means of taking better advantage of major corporate resources and of overcoming handicaps or weaknesses. A process of elimination is often helpful, because decisions by management that certain courses of action are undesirable may lead to positive definition of alternatives that offer promise.

The formulation of objectives is a major step in planning. In order that proposed projects may be examined in terms of these objectives, however, corresponding criteria should be developed. They involve definition of types of new undertakings that should be considered as means of reaching the goals, in- cluding market areas that appear attractive, categories of technology within the range of major skills of the staff, opportunities for more effective exploitation of raw material resources, etc.

Corporate objectives and criteria should be dynamic. They should be reviewed by management periodically, preferably at least semi-annually, to make sure that they are kept up to date. They require continual refinement in the light of experience in applying them to specific cases, and they need to be modified to take into account changes within the company as well as economic developments in the general economy.

Corporate Development Functions

The object of a corporate development program is to provide top man- agement of the company with comprehensive evaluations on which to base plans for making optimal use of resources in its efforts to attain defined objectives for profitability and growth. The following major functions are involved:

1. Definition of corporate objectives and continuing re- assessment of goals and criteria;

2. Coordination of information to aid the chief executive in evaluating plans and proposed programs for their implementation;

3. Planning and developing detailed programs to enable the company to attain the rates of profitability and growth set forth as objectives;

4. Reviewing corporate performance in comparison with plans.

Corporate planning is concerned with the analysis of growth opportunities for the company. It includes continuing review and analysis of strengths and weaknesses in market position, manufacturing capabilities, and technology. It also involves evaluation of proposed capital expenditures and their conformity to corporate plans, as well as analysis of alternative uses of financial resources. It develops procedures for checking actual performance against plans. It keeps the management alert to new or developing areas that may affect its policies or programs. Corporate planning should supply other departments of the company with economic and market intelligence to help them in evaluating their programs.

Acquisition studies comprise the formulation of criteria to be used in screening potential acquisitions, identification of candidate enterprises in the selected areas, assessment of proposed acquisitions as a measure for furthering corporate growth toward its objectives and preparation of supporting information for acquisition negotiations by management.

The acquisition route is often used by companies in industrialized countries as a means of accelerating the pace of corporate development. It may provide increased strength of management, enhanced marketing posture, greater depth of technology, improved manufacturing capability, better raw material position, or larger financial resources. While these reasons might superficially appear not to apply to enterprises in the public sector in developing countries, actually the same general type of analysis is useful in considering the merits of consolidating two or more operations in order to improve their combined efficiency.

Market research comprises the planning and implementation of systematic studies of customer needs, and the definition of potential markets for new, modified, or established products. Market research for new products differs from similar functions for established products in that it requires greater imagination and flexibility, and relies to a greater extent on non-routine methodology.

Market research should be distinguished from Sales analysis, the latter being concerned with the compilation and interpretation of market data relating to the company's existing product lines and distribution patterns. Sales analysis is an essential tool of marketing, and the function is therefore usually located within the marketing organization.

The term Marketing research is frequently used to denote the greater breadth that may be involved in studying requirements for entry into new types of markets.

Technical evaluation is concerned with appraisal of corporate development projects from the point of view of feasibility as to raw materials, technology, manufacturing requirements, and the present and projected market situation with respect to competitive products. This function is usually carried out in companies of intermediate size by the Research and Development Department, in cooperation with other pertinent groups, such as engineering, manufacturing, marketing, and technical service.

Economic evaluation involves the detailed estimation of capital requirements, operating costs, and profitability of major projects under consideration for corporate development, including comparison with alternative propositions. Such estimates should be made in increasing depth at advancing stages of progress of each project.

Market development is concerned with the organization and carrying out, usually in cooperation with existing marketing groups, of those steps involved in the introduction and initial penetration of commercial markets for new or modified products, or new markets or marketing approaches for existing products, until they have become suitably established to be taken over by the appropriate sales staffs.

Experience in industrialized countries, particularly in science-based industries, has revealed the difficulties inherent in trying to introduce innovative products solely through the use of the regular sales staff. The heavy demand for specialized knowledge about the new products and for abnormal amounts of time spent with selected customers in working out methods of use in their operations is often not compatible with the quotas, technical backgrounds, and schedules of line salesmen. When the products are related to the existing marketing pattern, responsibility for their introduction can be assigned to one or more technical salesmen (if the company has such a staff), but this means curtailing a corresponding amount of other activities. When the product is highly specialized, an individual may be selected to devote full time to acquiring the necessary technical background and then applying it in contacts with customers during the introductory period. He may report to marketing management, but, because the product is still in the development stage, there are advantages in having him assigned to the Corporate Development Department. When the product has attained the status of regular production and sales, responsibility is turned over to the appropriate marketing group, but it may still require much effort from technical salesmen and technical service personnel.

Job Description of a Director of Corporate Development

The following job description is given in detail as typical of the form in which responsibilities of the Corporate Development Department are defined in American practice. In order to carry out these functions, the Director should be a dynamic, objective individual with the ability and prestige necessary to select, mobilize, direct, and coordinate the pertinent activities to promote the progress of the company.

1. The Director of Corporate Development is responsible to the Chief Executive of the company.

2. The Director of Corporate Development, acting for and under the general direction of the Chief Executive of the company:

    a. Develops and conducts continuing review of corporate objectives and goals;

    b. Formulates criteria for evaluating projects in terms of corporate objectives;

    c. Develops programs for assessing corporate resources and performance as a basis for development plans;

    d. Formulates systematic plans for the achievement of corporate objectives and goals.

3. The Director of Corporate Development, in order to carry out the functions assigned to him by the Chief Executive:

    a. Organizes, staffs, and provides continuing direction for a small group to conduct the following activities of his Department, making use of specialized personnel in other departments of the company on a participative or consultative basis to the extent feasible: planning, acquisition studies, market research, technical evaluation, economic evaluation, and market development;

    b. Is responsible for the preparation of program proposals for the execution of corporate plans including acquisition studies;

    c. Organizes and directs corporate development activities on projects approved by the Chief Executive, using task forces wherever feasible;

    d. Conducts continuing assessment of company resources and performance as compared with plans;

    e. Reviews proposals for major capital expenditures to insure their conformity with corporate plans, and advises on their economic justification;

    f.   Evaluates major project proposals in comparison with alternative course of action;

    g.   Maintains cognizance of, and coordinates with overall corporate plans, other planning projects within the company, and encourages the initiation of such studies where needed;

    h.   Assists divisions and departments of the company in establishing and carrying out their own planning activities;

    i.   Seeks, investigates, and assesses outside opportunities for the company, including joint ventures, licenses, patents, and the like;

    j.   Undertakes special studies requested by the Chief Executive.

Relationship of Corporate Development to the Technical Department

Initial reaction of some technical directors to this job description may be that Corporate Development is taking over certain functions - particularly technical evaluation and economic evaluation - which are properly in the domain of Research and Development. In practice it turns out that the two departments are complementary rather than competitive. Corporate Development should be regarded as an extension of the functions of the Chief Executive which enables him to consider programs within the broader horizon of the enterprise as a whole rather than tending to limit himself to specific decisions on individual aspects of a project. This relieves the Technical Director of the need to involve himself in such questions as marketing, manufacturing and financial matters connected with new undertakings and permits him to concentrate on scientific and engineering development activities.

Further, since a premise of corporate development is to make use of specialized skills through project task forces, the input of technical evaluation will come from Research and Development, as will also much of the economic evaluation. Only as the workload becomes too heavy and involved will it be necessary to add specialists in these areas to the Corporate Development staff. Research and Development will remain the primary source of technical information and much economic data, and the task will be made easier through greater clarification of the requirements for specialized inputs of information as a result of the coordinative function supplied through Corporate Development.

Use of Corporate Objectives in Technical Programming

When the Chief Executive of the company has established plans for its development and expansion, he has provided the Technical Director with a general framework for reaching decisions as to the types of projects which conform to corporate goals and criteria.

In administering a technical program, however, corporate objectives and criteria are usually too general in character to provide adequate guidance for selection and implementation of projects. These objectives and criteria, insofar as they have technologic implications, should be redefined in terms of technical goals which reflect those areas in which the professional skills of the staff can be used most constructively. The act of framing the technical goals and obtaining approval of management as to their adequacy can exert potent influence in sharpening corporate objectives. Indeed, pressure from the Technical Director on management for guidance on major directions for future growth may lead to the initiation of systematic corporate planning.

Failure of management to provide this sort of guidance has resulted in much disillusionment in unsophisticated organizations. A new or expanded research activity may be set up in a wave of enthusiasm. Often the Technical Director suffers from an unduly heavy burden of responsibility for establishing an expensive program with an inadequate background of business aspects in the face of unreasonable, unexpressed, or inchoate expectations of management, particularly non-technical management. Neither side recognizes the hazard of lack of mutual understanding. Eventually managerial patience wears out, failure to produce profitable commercial results is blamed on the research administration, and drastic steps are likely to be taken.

CHAPTER **16**   CASE HISTORY OF
A TECHNICAL
PROGRAM

General Principles

In preceding chapters we have discussed the various types of functions
involved in the technical program as a whole, the role of management in providing
general guidance, and various procedures for aiding the formulation and execution
of projects, such as product policy and criteria, step-wise approach, and task
force operation.

In order to bring this material together to illustrate the manner in
which a coordinated technical program might be organized in a developing country,
a hypothetical case history seems a good procedure. The following example of
the addition of a polyvinyl acetate project to an existing polyvinyl chloride operation in the mythical country of Vigoria is therefore discussed in considerable
detail.

The cost figures cited for technical activities should not be taken as
representative of experience in any individual country, but only as estimates as
to the order of magnitude they might have in developing economies. To make clear
that they are not to be considered valid for any particular situation, they have been
left in U.S. dollars.

It should be pointed out that a new chemical operation in itself does not
provide many job opportunities, because the industry characteristically has a low
manpower-to-product volume ratio. However, because its products increase the
range of other types of manufactures, often with much higher employment potential, it may have a considerable impact on national development.

The cost of proposed commercial plant, sales potential, and pay-out
of the plant for polyvinyl acetate are hypothetical for the case of Vigoria. This
nation is assumed to have a population of 40,000,000, a rapidly developing economy, good technical resources, and a very favorable export position in its trade
with less highly developed countries in the area. These assumptions were made
to provide economic justification for a plant of this size.

Economic Background of the Enterprise

It is assumed that commercial production of polyvinyl chloride was
established in Vigoria five years ago, the plant and technical know-how having
been obtained abroad; that it has proved to be successful in filling a need in the
national economy; and that it is now so well established that the company is
ready for expansion. First we will review the steps that led to this encouraging
situation.

109

Economic Justification for polyvinyl chloride was provided several years ago by the demand that developed for articles made from imported material by various manufacturing operations in the country. The volume required in the future was expected to grow rapidly. In fact, potential use was already being restricted because the policy governing allocations of foreign exchange limited the funds available for purchase of the polymer and articles made from it. The market existed and fortunately other economic factors were favorable.

The original plant might have had over-capacity for the state of the economy except for two situations: (1) Because this was the only polyvinyl chloride plant in that part of the world, about half the production found its way in various forms into export to neighboring countries, thus establishing a balance of trade to permit purchase of other raw materials from them. (2) Because of the limited range of synthetic resins available, polyvinyl chloride enjoyed uses that might otherwise have been filled by competitive products.

Raw Materials required for the process selected were acetylene and hydrochloric acid. A large new hydroelectric power installation had just been completed some distance up a major river, and new undertakings were being considered to provide optimum use for electrical energy. The country needed more caustic soda, saponification of locally produced vegetable oils being a major consumer of this product, but if it were made by the electrolytic process, there was not then adequate use for the chlorine produced concurrently. This imbalance of chlorine versus caustic soda represents a situation commonly encountered in countries that are not highly industrialized; in industrial countries, on the other hand, demand for chlorine may become stronger than that for caustic soda.

Hydrogen as by-product from the electrolysis would be available, and hydrochloric acid could be made by direct combination of the two elements.

Calcium carbide would be required for generation of the acetylene, because there were no aliphatic hydrocarbon streams to consider as an alternative source. The country had recently installed an integrated iron and steel mill, with a battery of coking ovens, which could produce the required coke; freight costs to the hydroelectric site would be economic, because upriver loading of barges was not at capacity. (Transportation costs are an important factor in the marketing of heavy chemicals.) There was a good supply of limestone near the power.

Commercialization appeared justified and facilities were installed near the power site for calcium carbide, acetylene, and hydrochloric acid. These were piped "over the fence" to the vinyl chloride plant, which included units for making the monomer, for polymerization, and for the production of the intermediate products required by the local converting industry.

The general situation was in parallel with that which led to the installation of polyvinyl chloride operations in highly industrialized countries many years ago.

Planning the Technical Program

The technical staff was initially assembled well in advance of the completion of the plant. It consisted of the Technical Director, several technical men, and a group of non-professional assistants. They were trained in their functions with the help of a foreign expert with long experience in polyvinyl chloride technology. The first two years they were busily engaged in helping with problems connected with perfecting process and product. We will skip the details of how the technical program gradually expanded at the rate of about 15-20 percent per year, and begin our example with the status at the end of 1964, when the management decided to diversify into polyvinyl acetate.

We will assume that during the previous time the administration of technical functions was carried out in accordance with good administrative practices discussed in earlier chapters. The work was organized in a project system, and task forces were used wherever feasible.

The staff and work outline at the end of 1964, which agreed quite well with the plans developed in earlier years, is shown in Table 6.

Staff and Operating Costs. The total number of professional personnel had increased to 24 men. In accordance with the pattern for research and development which had evolved in the country, the non-professional staff had grown at a higher rate. In America, the ratio between professionals and non-professionals would have been about 1:1. In Western Europe, the ratio would probably have been 1:2.5 to 1:5, as it has been customary in many countries to operate with a lower percentage of professional personnel; one important reason for this difference is the availability in European countries of skilled non-professional technicians with an intermediate stage of technical education, a situation which is rarer in America, although it exists in some industrial centers.

TABLE 6

1964 PROGRAM AND MANPOWER ALLOCATIONS BEFORE
CONSIDERING VINYL ACETATE EXPANSION

| | Man-Years | | | |
	Professional	Non-professional Technicians	Clerical Maintenance	Total
Administration				
Administrative Staff	3.0	–	3.0	6.0
Library and Information	1.0	–	1.0	2.0
Facilities and Storeroom	–	–	7.0	7.0
Technical Service Functions				
Quality Control	1.0	4.0	1.0	6.0
Technical Service, Manufacturing	1.0	2.0	–	3.0
Technical Service, Marketing	3.0	5.0	1.0	9.0
Product Evaluation	2.0	6.0	1.0	9.0
Short-Range Program				
Development of New Items (Professional Time Distribution: Product A, 1.5; B, 1.0; C, 0.5; D, 0.6; E, 0.8; misc.0.6)	5.0	8.0	1.0	14.0
Process Improvement (Professional Time Distribution: Process F, 1.5; G, 1.0; misc.0.5)	3.0	10.0	1.0	14.0
Longer-Range Program				
Development of New Products (Professional Time Distribution: Product H, 1.5; J, 1.0; Exploratory 0.5)	3.0	3.0	–	6.0
Development of New Product Lines (Professional Time Distribution: Product K, 1.0; Exploratory 1.0)	2.0	1.0	–	3.0
Totals	24.0	39.0	16.0	79.0

The total operating cost of the laboratory, including all overhead factors such as equivalent of rental of space, is about four percent of total sales of the company, which is within the range to be expected for a synthetic resin operation under the assumptions of the example. The average cost of a technical-man-year turns out to be approximately $16,000. In America the cost would be considerably higher in a corresponding laboratory; in many, it runs as much as $35,000-40,000 per technical-man-year, or even more. In Western Europe the figures would be closer to those assumed in our example. It has been customary in the United States to use professional man-year costs for estimating expense of projects, but for international comparison, because of varying professional/non-professional ratios, expense per average-employee-year would be more logical. Table 7 quotes figures for research and development cost per scientist or engineer in the United States and the United Kingdom, and is taken from the O.E.C.D. report mentioned earlier. Salary and wage scales are much higher in the United States than in the United Kingdom, but because the ratio of non-professional to professional employees is higher in the latter country, the parallelism in the table is closer than would be expected.

TABLE 7

COST OF RESEARCH AND DEVELOPMENT PER SCIENTIST OR ENGINEER

	United States 1959 $	United Kingdom 1961 £
Group A		
Aircraft	41,300	32,200
Vehicles	49,300	15,200
Electronics	33,700	10,700
Other electrical	40,500	9,800
Machinery	32,300	9,400
Instruments	28,100	8,300
Chemicals[1]	30,700	6,500
Group B		
Rubber	23,600	--
Ferrous metals	26,500	5,900
Non-ferrous metals	25,700	7,200
Metal products	26,100	--
Stone, clay and glass	25,500	
Paper	20,600	6,900
Group C		
Food	21,700	7,200
Textiles and apparel	24,100	7,300
Lumber and furniture	23,500	
Other manufacturing	25,900	6,900
Total all industries	35,200	11,900

1. Excluding petroleum refining.

Laboratory Facilities were projected, when the building was planned, on the basis of 600 square feet per professional man, to allow room for expansion in staff. About 60 percent of the total of 15,000 square feet, provided to accommodate the technical staff of 25 projected for 1964, is working space, the balance being occupied by general offices, library, wash and locker rooms, shops, storerooms, and corridors. When occupancy approaches an average of 250 square feet per technical man in the United States, accommodations are usually reasonable, although this depends on the type of work involved, but below this it begins to get crowded. Space requirements calculated on a professional man average would need to be modified according to experience in countries using larger ratios of non-professional to professional.

The cost of the bare laboratory building--without any laboratory furniture, plumbing, or equipment--was $30 per square foot in the country assumed in our example, making a total cost of $450,000. This cost was 25 percent over the estimate, as is frequently the case for research structures, because of over-optimistic forecasts and numerous changes in plans requested during construction. The cumulative investment in furniture, utilities, fixtures, and equipment was about $350,000 at the beginning of 1964.

Program and Work Assignments

The general scheme of operations is shown in Table 6, together with manpower allocated to the different functions and types of work. Table 6 should be self-explanatory, but the following points should be noted.

The terms new items, new products, and new product lines are used in the sense of the definitions given in a previous chapter. The fact that emphasis is heavy on "defensive" projects is characteristic of a relatively new undertaking, which needs to consolidate its technical posture. As the work becomes more innovative in character, the input of professional talents often becomes higher in proportion to non-professional. This is because emphasis needs to be put on trained observation and interpretation of phenomena.

Program and Budget Preparation for 1965

Corporate Development Policies were formulated by the management as a result of a planning program instituted early in 1963. The studies led to the following conclusions regarding product policies:

1. Polyvinyl acetate, which is the subject of New Product Project H
    in the preceding program tabulation, has a promising future in
    Vigoria, and several large new uses have developed, either for
    the homopolymer or the copolymer with polyvinyl chloride. The
    adjacent calcium carbide-acetylene enterprise is planning to
    install a synthetic acetic anhydride and acetic acid operation, so
    that, fortunately for the complexity of the present illustrative
    example, we need not include this new technology in our discus-
    sion. This neighboring plant can justify the expansion in scope
    of products, which would upgrade its technology, because it can
    count on another major customer, namely, the viscose rayon
    enterprise, established in Vigoria some years ago; it is planning
    to undertake the production of cellulose acetate, which would ex-
    pand the range of fibres available to the textile industry, and of
    plastics for other types of manufacture. (Polyvinyl acetate has
    been classified as a new product rather than as a new product
    line.)

2. The research and development staff and the engineering staff have
    developed sufficient skill and technical background to undertake
    the development, and assistance from abroad would be a secondary
    requirement. Certain major items of equipment and instrumenta-
    tion would need to be purchased from foreign sources, but the
    specifications would be developed internally.

3. The company is planning to enter two other synthetic resin opera-
    tions later on--phenol-formaldehyde and urea-formaldehyde--there-
    fore active research projects (now represented by New Product Line
    Project K for urea-formaldehyde, while work on phenolics has been
    exploratory) should be maintained. Interest in ureas will be stim-
    ulated by tentative plans of one of the synthetic nitrogen fertilizer
    plants to add synthetic urea to its product line.

4. The carrying out of the product and process development, applica-
    tion research, pilot plant studies, and design of commercial plant
    will represent a large demand on technical resources of the enter-
    prise. An estimate of the magnitude of effort necessary will be
    covered in a later section.

5. Because of this new project, the present program should be re-
    evaluated to see whether or not some of the activities can be
    compressed.

Revision of the Technical Program

Preliminary proposals for the 1965 program showed (as is frequently the case with research and development activities) requests for expansion of present projects, some additional projects, but a considerable increase to take care of polyvinyl acetate. After much discussion with operating and staff groups, the following conclusions were reached with management:

1. Technical service to manufacturing could be reduced on polyvinyl chloride, because the plant is operating smoothly; the balance of the service effort could be transferred to the acetate project.

2. Technical service to marketing could be curtailed because of the accumulated back-log of technical information and the greater experience that customers have had in using polyvinyl chloride. The service could be improved if one of the technical men who is skilled in solving customers' problems were transferred to the marketing staff as a technical salesman.

3. Quality control and product evaluation should remain little changed, but some time should be made available for problems connected with the acetate.

4. In the new items program, Product A work has been completed and the product should be put into production. Product E turned out to be difficult and the project should be changed to a new product project (Product L) with more effort. Two additional new item projects are needed (Products M and N).

5. In process improvement work, Process F is ready for transfer to the plant and should be closed as a project.

6. In the new products program, Product H is the polyvinyl acetate which is being consolidated with the broader development study. Project J is concerned with a new type of formulation and should be continued, as should also the exploratory work.

7. In work on new product lines, Product K is the urea-formaldehyde work, which should be continued, as well as the allocation for exploratory work, but experiments on phenol-formaldehyde should be converted from this classification to a project on New Product Line O. A new application research project (Product K_1) on urea-formaldehydes should be started as an extra-mural study in a central contract research laboratory, because broader contacts with other projects supported by companies in different industries would be advantageous for development of new uses.

8. Work projected for 1965 on the development of Product H, poly-vinyl acetate, was as follows:

Quality Control Methodology

Evaluation Methodology

Product Development

Process Development

Pilot Plant Design and Start
of Installation

Application Research

These changes in program and assignment of staff are reflected in Table 8. The technical staff is to be increased by one-quarter during the year. Recruitment and indoctrination of this many individuals will impose a fairly heavy load on the laboratory administration.

Estimation of Activities to Commercialize Product H

Before deciding to move polyvinyl acetate from applied research into product and process development stage, the management had an estimate made of the technical effort and time required to reach commercial production. This furnishes a practical example of Figure 2, "Technical Manpower Involved in a Typical Project." Nearly two years had elapsed since the project was started in the laboratory, and three technical-man-years of effort had already been ex-pended in the applied research stage. Additional expenditure of technical time, shown in detail at the conclusion of this chapter, is estimated at 30 technical-man-years spread over a period of 27 months.

Basis of Estimate was established in a memorandum, covering the following points:

1. Technology is obtainable through the skills of the staff, with minor assistance from foreign sources in certain areas. There is much information in the literature, plus many special reports received from equipment suppliers, and still further information developed through personal contacts with foreign manufacturers; all of this information has been carefully analyzed. The research staff includes two men who had research experience abroad on polyvinyl acetate. Applied research, evaluation of laboratory samples, and preliminary cost analyses have not revealed any major difficulties or hazards to success.

TABLE 8

1965 REVISED PROGRAM AND MANPOWER ALLOCATIONS TO PROVIDE
FOR EXPANDED POLYVINYL ACETATE WORK

	Man Years				
	Professional	Non-professional Technicians	Clerical, Maintenance	Total	Change from 1964
Administration					
Administrative Staff	3.0	–	3.0	6.0	–
Library and Information	1.0	–	1.0	2.0	–
Facilities and Storeroom	–	–	8.0	8.0	(+1.0)
Technical Service Functions					
Quality Control	0.8	3.5	1.0	5.3	(-0.7)
Technical Service, Manufacturing	0.7	1.5	–	2.2	(-0.8)
Technical Service, Marketing	2.0	4.0	1.0	7.0	(-2.0)
Product Evaluation	1.7	5.5	1.0	8.2	(-0.8)
Short-Range Program					
Development of New Items	5.0	8.0	1.0	14.0	–
(Professional Time Distribution: Product $\underline{B}$, 1.5; $\underline{C}$, 1.1; $\underline{D}$, 1.3; $\underline{M}$, 0.7; $\underline{N}$, 0.3; Misc., 0.5)					
Process Improvement	2.0	8.0	1.0	11.0	(-3.0)
(Professional Time Distribution: Process $\underline{G}$, 1.5; Misc., 0.5)					
Longer-Range Program					
Development of New Products	3.0	3.0	–	6.0	–
(Product $\underline{J}$, 1.5; $\underline{L}$, 1.0; Exploratory, 0.5)					
Development of New Product	4.0	3.0	–	7.0	(+4.0)
Lines (Product $\underline{K}$, 2.0; $\underline{O}$, 1.0; Exploratory, 1.0)					
Extra-Mural Project					
Application Research,	1.0	1.0	–	2.0	(+2.0)
Product $\underline{K}_1$					
Sub-total	24.2	37.5	17.0	78.7	(-0.3)
Polyvinyl Acetate					
(Product $\underline{H}$)					
Quality Control Methodology	0.2	0.5	–	0.7	
Evaluation Methodology	0.3	0.5	–	0.8	
Product Development	3.0	3.5	1.0	7.5	
Process Development	2.8	6.0	1.0	9.8	
Pilot Plant Design	1.5	–	–	1.5	
(work carried out chiefly in Engineering Department)					
Application Work, Extra-Mural	1.0	2.0	–	3.0	
Sub-total	8.8	12.5	2.0	23.3	
Total	33.0	50.0	19.0	102.0	+23.0

2. Assuming that product and process development work continues to
    be favorable, the pilot plant will be designed to one-tenth commer-
    cial scale. This is a rule-of-thumb guide for magnitude of scale-up
    of a new process in progressing from stage to stage. When a new
    item or a new product involves only minor modification from estab-
    lished technology, it is often considered safe to jump directly from
    large glassware to commercial equipment, because the cost repre-
    sented by one or two partially unsuccessful batches may be less
    significant than the time and expense of work on intermediate scale.
    Other examples lying between these extremes need to be considered
    individually.

    The pilot plant is to be used for producing sample quantities of
    materials, to develop customer interest and experience, only to
    the extent deemed advisable to stimulate market demand. Use of
    this scale to produce large quantities of material would prove costly
    if expense is properly analyzed, a fact which many companies fail
    to recognize. Further, pilot plant samples may not be identical
    with final commercial product, a situation which can damage rela-
    tions with customers.

    The pilot plant is to be designed to provide considerable flexibility
    and will be kept in stand-by condition after development work is
    completed because of probable need later on.

3. The Engineering Department will act as general contractor, will
    design and install the pilot plant (using special equipment and in-
    struments purchased abroad), will prepare all flow diagrams and
    supervise all detailed drawings for commercial plant, for which
    latter purpose the drafting room staff of the local engineering
    construction firm will be used, in order to avoid the necessity of
    building up a temporary staff of draftsmen. The engineering con-
    struction firm, under supervision of the project engineer from the
    Engineering Department, will prepare the site, erect all buildings,
    and install all equipment.

The estimated cost of the pilot plant is $150,000, and the expense of
materials, utilities, depreciation, and miscellaneous expense and overhead--
except salaries and wages--is budgeted at $50,000.

The preliminary cost estimate of the commercial plant is $4,000,000,
with an additional $1,250,000 of working capital to finance inventory of raw ma-
terials, intermediates, finished product, and miscellaneous supplies, as well as
accounts receivable and extra expense of start-up, etc. Engineering expense for
the commercial plant is estimated at 12 percent of installed cost.

At the projected selling price of the products, the return on investment will give a pay-out of the plant in 2.8 years.

Schedule of Technical Activities was prepared in order to program allocation of staff to the project. A forecast of the number of technical-man-years required is shown in Table 9. Because the different phases can in part be carried on concurrently, the final column of Table 9, which shows the net estimated time, provides for overlap.

TABLE 9

TECHNICAL-MAN-YEAR SCHEDULE TO COMMERCIALIZE POLYVINYL ACETATE (PROJECT H)

Phase	Total TMY	Period (months)	Elapsed Time (months)
Product Development and Evaluation	5.0	24	
Process Development	3.5		
Design, Installation, and Operation of Pilot Plant	7.0		9
Field Tests of Product	2.0		
Product Evaluation of Samples from Pilot Plant and Commerical Installation	1.5	18	
Assistance from Product Development	1.0		
Design, Installation, and Adjustment of Commercial Plant	10.0	18	18
Totals	30		27

The cost of this technical effort (excluding expense of pilot plant materials, services, and overhead, which were mentioned in a previous section) was estimated on the basis of the average figure of $16,000 per technical-man-year mentioned earlier, giving a total of $480,000 for the schedule shown in Table 9. The management recognized that it should probably use different factors for laboratory work, pilot plant operation, and design engineering, but did not have data to calculate them, because this is its first experience with a comprehensive project of this kind. The accounting department was asked to develop a plan to accumulate costs separately for these different activities, so that in the future the company would have a better basis for project estimates.

CHAPTER 17

COMMERCIAL DEVELOPMENT
AS A MEASURE OF
CORPORATE TECHNOLOGY

Background

The critical importance of technical progress and the rising cost of obtaining it have created a demand for a method of measuring research and development. The various schemes proposed have not received wide acceptance. They have been handicapped by arbitrary compromises in estimated profits from research, because they have usually been worked out as a means of defending the research budget. On the other hand, improved methods for evaluating the economics of individual projects are being developed and applied.

Assessment of the technical program as a whole remains subjective: it may be good but poorly utilized; it may be mediocre but well exploited. The success of excellent research projects may be nullified by failure of the company to implement the results. In many cases, attention should be directed to improving management planning for technical guidance and for application of new technology rather than to harassing the research department. From the point of view of operating departments, what they frequently expect from research is not innovative new products, which entail departure from existing sales and manufacturing patterns, but miracles which will make higher profits with only minor additional effort.

Data handling to aid managerial planning has nevertheless been improving in many other activities. If we have not been able to propose a yardstick for research and development, perhaps we have been trying to measure the wrong thing.

Analysis and Projection of Technical Contributions to Profitability

In the belief that a yardstick is urgently needed for measuring benefits from technical programs, the author presented at a meeting of the Commercial Chemical Development Association in March 1964 the concept of "Analysis and Projection of Technical Contributions to Profitability" (APTeC). It consists of comparing the use a company makes of its technology in creating sales and profits - which is the essence of corporate development - with the cost of generating this technology.

APTeC does not purport to be a direct measurement of the effectiveness of research and development. Most research executives feel this can be done only on a subjective basis; the author agrees with this view. Instead, APTeC

is addressed to estimation of the impact of new technology on the performance
of the company as an organization. In this sense, it adds a new dimension to
corporate planning.

The procedure consists of analysis of sales and profit figures for four
product groupings, using the classification described in Chapter V. The groups
are: (1) basic line, (2) new items, (3) new products, and (4) new product lines.
Associated technical expense is then analyzed by the same classification, and
ratios of this expense to sales and profits are calculated to provide a measure
of the relationship between the technology employed and the commercial benefits
obtained for the three classes of products showing progressive degrees of innovation.

Advantages of this method of analysis are the following:

1. It establishes documentation for the formulation
    of plans for corporate development.

2. It provides factual background for institution or
    revision of corporate product policies.

3. It gives management a clearer understanding of
    past performance and future potential of technical
    programs, and thus provides a basis for more in-
    cisive analysis.

4. It encourages more effective use of technical re-
    sources by the rest of the organization.

The concept of APTeC is to reveal the relationship between cause and
effect in regard to creation and use of new technology. Certainly good management demands careful analysis of sales and profitability of all segments of the
product line. Certainly good management requires critical review of the distribution of effort in the technical program. Can these two sets of data be corre-
lated?

A needed element is a more meaningful classification of the goals of
technical projects. This would permit interpretation in terms of degree of risk
and proportionate rewards for innovation. A scheme for filling this gap is dif-
ferentiation among "new items," innovative "new products," and "new product
lines" (i.e., new businesses), through the use of definitions and criteria which
were presented in the chapter on "Corporate Logistics and Product Policy."

APTeC uses historical analysis of sales and profitability versus technical expense for the basic product line and these three classes of added products as a frame of reference for estimating future impact of anticipated new technology. Allowance is made for different time lags in implementing projects corresponding to the magnitude of technical effort required.

APTeC is obviously not the major tool that management needs for evaluating corporate posture and outlook, because it is directed only toward the effect of the technical component. In the form here proposed, it does not take into account the changes in the actual volume of profits and sales, which are necessarily management's major concern. Nevertheless, the generation and implementation of technology are so vital in the future of the company that they should carry a high priority in managerial analysis.

The APTeC procedures have been discussed with a number of executives who are evolving their own systems of evaluation of technical activities. This method could serve as an extension of most of these schemes, and is more comprehensive than any of which the author has knowledge.

The system as described here is centered on product development, because this is the dominant purpose of most research programs. Process development, from this point of view, is really product-oriented in that its objective is to make products better or more cheaply.

Classification of Added Products

Many managements are not aware that a large share of the technical budget is expended in defensive work necessary to maintain the competitive position of the company. Research and development, instead of being aimed at innovative products with attractive margins, may be concentrated on those that fit neatly into the existing product line, with little strain on marketing or manufacturing resources, and often little change in the degree of profitability. Defensive technology is devoted to new items for the present product line, process improvement, and technical service to sales and production. Aggressive research, on the other hand, has as its goal the attainment of an enhanced profit position through introduction of innovative new products, new product lines, new processes, or major new uses for present products.

In the following discussion, the terminology used for added products will follow the definitions given in Chapter V, which are repeated here for convenience.

1. New items are products which are closely related to
    the present line and which can be marketed with little
    change in marketing channels, service, or strategy;

2. New products are innovative in character and enable
    the company to offer materials to satisfy customers'
    needs in a more effective way but still are within the
    marketing areas already being served; they require
    more extensive service to show the customer how
    they can best be used.

3. New product lines are new businesses which lead the
    company into entirely new marketing areas and re-
    quire a different distribution strategy and organization.

Historical Analysis of Added Products

To set a basis for forecasting anticipated benefits from the technical
program, the experience record of the company for profit and sales performance
for the existing line and the three classes of added products versus the associated
technical expense should be compiled for a period of years. Five years should be
adequate in most cases. If the impact of basic research is to be included in the
analysis, ten years would be better, in order to allow for a greater time lag in
commercialization of results. This tabulation, in addition to disclosing trends
in the past effect of different classes of added products, will develop the methodology for classifying and collecting data for continuation of the system.

The method of computing profit data for use in APTeC will depend on
the accounting system preferred by the company, but some of the implications of
the effect of the method on numerical values of profit-to-technical expense ratios
should be pointed out. Use of gross profit before divisional and/or corporate
sales and general overheads and before taxes will give the most direct comparison;
gross profit avoids the bias that may be imparted by lower sales costs for older
products. If net profit before taxes is employed, all technical expense will have
been deducted, which causes some distortion. If profit after taxes is used, the
distortion will be greater, because technical expense will have been charged off
as an operating cost, as in the preceding case, and therefore will not have been
adjusted on the basis of a tax credit. Further, for illustrative purposes in the
examples given later, it has been assumed that large items of technical expense
connected with start-up of new operations have been capitalized, so that their effect is distributed over a period of years, rather than being concentrated at the
time of initial operation. Using a rolling three-year average for sales, profits,
and technical expense would have an advantage in establishing smoother trend
lines.

The initial step, therefore, is to assemble data for sales and profits over a five-year period for the four different classes of products. While individual products within these groups will show wide variation in sales and profit history and outlook, they will have sufficient homogeneity in marketing characteristics for examination of the effect of the technologic component. In companies with a divisional structure, the figures for the product groups should be compiled on the basis of individual divisions.

For collection of technical costs segregated by product groups, a considerable amount of estimation will be required, because most laboratories have not done their record keeping on a comparable classification. The actual breakdown should be estimated by people at the working level on the basis established by technical management. In passing, it should be added that in many laboratories the assumed technical costs are not realistic because they do not include all associated overheads. It is recommended that for APTeC the accumulated technical costs should be as inclusive as possible; subsequently, if it is desirable to analyze costs of technical service or some other activity, this can be carried out separately. It is recommended further that technical expense be collected on a basis that will allow for the time lag in commercializing results from research and development directed at the three classes of added products; it is suggested that for comparisons on new items one year be allowed, two years for new products, and three years for new product lines, but the experience of an individual company may warrant a different time scale.

A practical procedure for making breakdowns of technical expense is not hard to develop, and from personal experience it by no means represents the tremendous chore that might be feared. Aside from its use in the APTeC plan, classification of technical costs in this manner is worth the effort in its own right for the purpose of critical review of the directions in which the technical budget is being expended. When the general scheme has been established, accumulation of future technical costs can be made on the same basis, and as time goes on the figures will become more meaningful in program analysis.

The final objective is to prepare general summaries from product group data, on a corporate or divisional basis, showing the relations as percentages of past benefits (volume and profit) incurred as technical expense. These summaries would take the form illustrated in Table 10.

The question will arise as to how long individual new items and new products should be carried separately before they are merged into their respective product lines. This is a matter for decision in the individual company as to the period of separation which serves a useful purpose. At least five years would be advisable to provide a good record of experience.

TABLE 10

PAST BENEFITS VERSUS TECHNICAL EXPENSE

Typical figures which might be found by this analysis are given below. These express the percentages of sales and profit represented by technical expense. They are cited to illustrate the experience of a company with the following characteristics:

Basic Product Line: Technical expense 2% of sales, profit 10% of sales before taxes.

New Items: Technical expense 2.4% of sales, profit 11% of sales before taxes, i.e., performance similar to established products.

New Products: Technical expense dropping successively from 6% of sales to 3% on individual products, profit 15% of sales before taxes (this profit level necessary to justify introduction of new products), with performance improving as heavier expenses of initial introduction become smaller in relation to sales and profit, and further improvement is to be expected.

New Product Lines: Technical expense, after commercialization begins, gradually drops from a high percentage of sales, while profit increases from loss during start-up to 20% of sales before taxes (this profit level required to warrant entry into a new business), with still better performance in sight.

Percentages of Sales and Profit Represented by Technical Expense are accumulated by using time lag of one year for implementation of technology in the case of new items, two years for new products, and three years for new product lines.

	$\dfrac{\text{Technical Expense}}{\text{Sales}} \times 100$				$\dfrac{\text{Technical Expense}}{\text{Profit}} \times 100$			
	Basic Prod. Line	New Items	New Prods.	New Prod. Lines	Basic Prod. Line	New Items	New Prods.	New Prod. Lines
1959		New Product Introduced and New Product Line Started						
	2.1%	2.4%	7.2%	Start-up	19%	21%	40%	Loss
1960	1.9	2.3	4.3	58%	20	19	28	80%
1961		Another New Product Introduced						
	2.0	2.6	6.0	16	18	20	37	45
1962	2.2	2.4	3.3	9.1	20	20	30	31
1963	2.1	2.3	3.0	6.9	19	21	25	28

The new product lines will become established as separate businesses and they in turn will require programs directed at new items and new products. The same scheme as used in the initial analysis should be used for them to obtain the corresponding data on benefits versus technical costs. In other words, they become new divisions of the company, and have their own pattern of basic line, new items, and new products.

Methodology for Forecasting

Many companies have developed systems for estimating future profitability of major technical projects, and quite a number of these have been described in the literature. Such techniques as discounted cash flow are being used to give a more realistic appraisal of the profit expected from the investment in a new operation as compared with a normal return from conventional capital utilization.

Use of APTeC methodology does not require change in project evaluation procedures. In fact, it extends their usefulness by fitting them into a larger framework of experience-based projection of the effect of the entire technical program.

Forecasting should be handled under the product classifications described earlier. The example of forecasts will be incorporated in a summary resembling the historical table.

The tabulations start with percentages of technical-expense/sales and technical-expense/profit projections for the basic product line, and the estimates made for these figures in the normal course of corporate planning will suffice for the purpose.

It is likely that most companies will have considerable regularity of flow of new items into the product line. If this assumption holds in an individual situation, the experience of the historical five-year period will establish trend lines which show fair degree of fit to the data. Unless there is a decided change in the company's product policy or an important market variation, it is reasonable to expect that the technical-expense/sales and technical-expense/profit percentages will continue along the trend lines for at least two or three years.

Hopefully, a company will enjoy a healthy record of introduction of innovative new products. If this is the case, past experience should permit projection of trend lines for this classification. If no upward trend is apparent, the management should take steps to encourage innovation in its research program. In Table 11 the number of new products introduced is purposely kept small.

TABLE 11

PROJECTION OF SALES AND PROFITS VERSUS TECHNICAL EXPENSE
OF ADDED PRODUCTS

The figures illustrate the outlook that might be projected for the company whose history was shown in the preceding table. The data express percentages of technical expense in relation to sales and profit when the following experience is expected:

Basic Product Line: Sales declining slightly, with technical expense rising above 2% because of diminishing volume, profit declining to 9% of sales before taxes.

New Items: About the same sales and profit performance as for basic product line, but new items are showing less impact.

New Products: Technical expense 3-4% of sales, profit 15% of sales, better performance than before, but special expense to be incurred in introducing a new product in 1965 is expected to influence over-all performance adversely that year.

New Product Lines: The new product line started in 1959 continues to improve, but a second new product line is expected to begin operation 1966 and higher technical expenses will set back performance that year. In practice, the new product lines would be analyzed separately.

Percentages of Sales and Profits Represented by Technical Expense are estimated with the same time lag that was used in the previous table, viz., one year for new items, two years for new products, and three years for new product lines.

$$\frac{\text{Technical Expense}}{\text{Sales}} \times 100$$

	Basic Prod. Line	New Items	New Prods.	New Prod. Lines	Basic Prod. Line	New Items	New Prods.	New Prod. Lines
1964	2.2%	2.0%	2.5%	4.3%	20%	19%	18%	26%
1965			Another New Product Introduced					
	2.2	2.3	4.6	3.7	22	21	26	24
1966			Another New Product Line Started					
	2.3	2.4	3.1	5.8	25	24	21	34
1967	(2.4?)	(2.5?)	2.8	3.9	(28?)	(26?)	20	23

Finally, since new product lines are to be treated as separate divisions of the company's business, and can be expected to show up at rarer intervals, there will probably be little regularity in their emergence. Each will show its own pattern of technical-expense/sales and technical-expense/profit ratios. The figures will show the impact of major diversification on profitability.

The columns of data in Tables 10 and 11 for technical expense as percent of profits are useful in that form for critical examination of the technical program, because percentages are the usual method of looking at these relationships. The reciprocals of these figures, however, may be better suited for general managerial purposes, because it is easier to see from them the fact that technical expense may continue to be at higher rates for new products and new product lines, as compared with the basic line and new items, but still result in a greater contribution because of greater profitability.

Use of APTeC in Evaluating Corporate Technical Postures

The following brief sketches provide examples of the application of APTeC to planning for corporate development.

Company A, Complacence, Inc., shows, when management examines over-all performance figures, a static situation in volume, and declining profit. Two new products introduced in 1960, but based on work done considerably earlier, have grown and have made money. APTeC analysis reveals that technical expense ratios are rising in a disturbing manner for the old line and added items, and in fact are higher than for the successful new products. No other new products are in immediate view. Moral: Company A had better embark on an aggressive program to get new technology.

Company B, Steadfast and Company, has expanded its regular product line, has maintained steady profitability, and is regarded as a leader in its industry. APTeC figures show little change in technical expense ratios for its original product line and added new items, but there have not been enough innovations in several years to project a trend for new products. Diagnosis: Company B has exploited its technology to excellent advantage and the short-term outlook is good, because it could not hold its position if competitors were introducing many new products. Within a few years, however, it may have exhausted the potential of its product line and now is the time to look for diversification through a major internal effort or acquisition.

Company C, Lively Associated Industries, has introduced a succession of innovative new products and new product lines which it has quickly exploited. Because of technical leadership in its industry, it capitalizes on its ability to move rapidly into new product areas. Its APTeC ratios for new products and new lines continue to remain very much higher than those for the original line and added items (which are nevertheless showing excellent profit performance), and they give no evidence of declining. On careful consideration, it does not appear that such high ratios are characteristic of its field of industry. Question: is its program of innovation dominating its policies at the expense of putting adequate emphasis on exploiting in greater depth the commercial potential of its impressive store of technology?

CHAPTER **18**   SUMMARY OF
ADMINISTRATIVE
PRINCIPLES

General Objectives of Technical Administration

In preceding chapters, managerial aspects of technical programs have been discussed in relation to particular subjects. This final chapter ties together the broad principles that have been illustrated in various sections and touches briefly on other pertinent topics.

Emphasis has been placed on the fact that the basic asset for carrying out a technical program is the collection of talents and skills of scientific and engineering personnel. The aim of such administrative devices as project systems and task forces is to promote the direct involvement of staff members in solving problems that have a logical relationship to the objectives of the organization. Vagueness or uncertainty about the justification and utilization of work surely leads to confusion and frustration of individuals in their identification of themselves with the forward movement of the commercial, Government, or institutional enterprise which has assumed the responsibility of supporting their efforts.

Most individuals in a large organization feel the needs of two kinds of personal relationships: The first is a defined place in the hierarchy with a direct contact with a representative of the managerial chain of command to whom to look for the formal needs of an employee on matters that may be broadly grouped as personnel administration. The second is the coordination of participation in technical activities to attain professional fulfillment. In a formal administrative pattern, the two functions will usually be the responsibility of the immediate superior. In a task force system, they are separated in theory and often in practice in a manner which elevates the dignity of technical performance by divorcing it from the role of subordination to an organizational superior.

Enlarging on the first or organization-oriented type of relationship, the administrative supervisor is the direct contact through which the individual finds his place in the enterprise family. This is the person to whom he looks for assurance that the general atmosphere of his employment is such as to promote the use of his technical abilities. The supervisor is normally the key figure in determining his orientation in the corporate community, including not only the definition and recognition of status, but also the system by which working relationships with others are clarified and implemented. He is the one to whom to turn in regard to personal aspects of employment, working conditions, and particularly in guidance on professional performance and development. He is the official contact for matters relating to other echelons. When this relationship to the supervisor is not clear, the individual may feel himself adrift in the organization.

In regard to the second or work-oriented type of relationship, a sense of purpose and responsibility is peculiarly important for technical personnel. The results are usually intangible, because they take the form of reports or memoranda relating to actual operations with which the individual has little direct contact. This situation is, of course, also true of other staff functions. By contrast, in the operating activities of manufacturing and marketing, a person can identify himself with the actual movement of products. Even in more abstract areas such as accounting, the output is directly intertwined with operations and the need for the service is clearly apparent for the financial control of the business. But there is no accepted method for objective evaluation of the results of research and development and hence those involved profit from closer association with the implementation of their work.

Instilling a sense of purpose is therefore a prime requisite for good technical management. The informal organization employed in task force operation is an important aid in this direction, because it extends and re-enforces the participation of the individual into the realm of implementation. The institution of corporate objectives and criteria, and the adoption of systematic programming of technical activities, create a general atmosphere of confidence that the projects, whether successful or not, were at least conceived for defined, evaluated goals.

Technical departments should therefore be active participants with other groups in the company in matters to which they can contribute. They should seek guidance from management and cooperation from operating staff. They should be alert for technical information affecting the business of the company and should transmit this information through appropriate channels.

It is often said that laboratory managers will obtain best results from their staffs if they lead them rather than try to direct them. Men at the working level have the best understanding of the phenomena with which they are involved, and positive recognition of this fact is essential for high morale. Continuous effort should be made to keep them abreast of objectives and criteria for their projects, so that they can feel responsibility for interpreting results and planning new experiments within this framework and with an attitude of professional involvement.

Personnel Administration

A major function of the Technical Director is to set good procedures to recruit, train, develop, and inspire his staff. He should be alert to policies, or lack of policies, that contribute to ineffective working conditions. He should uncover sources of irritation among the staff in order to try to correct them.

The Technical Director should make a point of having each new man in his department properly informed of company and laboratory policies and regulations. He should see to it that knowledge of changes in such matters is imparted directly, rather than through accidental channels. He should try to have the men, particularly those just starting their careers, exposed to different types of work in order that he may learn the directions in which their interests and talents lie. He should encourage all those who are so inclined to improve their professional stature through organized or individual study.

Each member of the staff should be given a personal performance review periodically, preferably by his immediate supervisor and at least once a year. The discussions should be frank, and should cover both strong and weak points. Organizations often have stated policies requiring performance reviews, but in practice may allow supervisors to conduct them in such fashion that they have little effect. Credit should be given to those who make valuable contributions to their projects, and announcements regarding such commendation should be given publicity, internal or external, appropriate to the case.

In short, the policies should promote professional pride of the individual and of the organization with which he is associated.

Reports

The individuals who are likely to derive most direct benefit from reports are those who prepare them. The report is a means of: (1) establishing a record of personal performance; (2) preparing the way for projection of required future work through summary and analysis of present status; and (3) clarifying the situation on the project to establish a basis for continuation, expansion, contraction, or abandonment, so that those involved are either assured of managerial interest in the immediate program or are given more promising tasks. In brief, good reports are the means by which to secure recognition and to play an important role in obtaining challenging work assignments.

The requirements for reports on industrial projects are quite different from those used in academic studies. In the latter, it is customary to define the background in some detail, to point out theoretical implications, to trace in historical order the scientific problems that had to be overcome, and to record experimental results at such length that they can be repeated by others. In industrial research reports, the emphasis is to provide a basis for decision on future course of action. Practice varies in different organizations, but in many the following sequence is followed: (1) A very concise statement of conclusions and recommendations, suitable for the information of a busy executive; (2) a longer statement, but still concise, of the basis of the conclusions and recommendations; (3) discussion and analysis of the work in sufficient detail to support the previous statement, but in logical order to provide a basis for the sequence of steps in the conclusion, rather than in historical order; (4) appendices of essential data required to permit analysis and verification of the conclusions.

Technical reports are prepared in various forms to serve different purposes:

Progress Reports on all projects are usually required on a regular basis, monthly or weekly, in most research organizations. These have as major purpose informing the department managers of the status of the work, noteworthy conclusions, and plans for continuation.

Management Summaries are used in some companies, usually every month or quarter, to give the general executives a very brief summary of the status of the program.

Interim Reports on individual projects are prepared as needed to summarize progress on one or more phases which have reached a conclusive stage, in order that the work to date may be recorded in organized form. They often serve the purpose of giving groups concerned with other aspects of the project needed details. If regular progress reports have been written in suitable manner, they can be employed to lighten the burden of preparing interim reports.

Final Reports are usually written to summarize all information needed for implementation of a project, or when the work is not to be utilized at the time, to record the results for future reference.

Program Review

Emphasis has been placed in preceding chapters on the need for continuing review of the total program on a regular schedule, which should be at least quarterly. Use of a project system backed up by effective reports serves to focus attention on defined objectives and the status of progress toward these goals. It encourages concentration on each topic commensurate with its importance. It facilitates establishment of priorities in matching personnel resources against urgency. It promotes readjustment of program to reflect interim changes in corporate requirements.

A comprehensive project system also sets the stage for more objective analysis of requirements for defensive work. Because of the glamor of longer range programs leading to innovation, major attention is likely to be devoted to them, with corresponding reduction in intensity of review of shorter-range work on development of new items, product and process improvement, and technical service. It has been pointed out that these activities are likely to account for more than half the total program. If they are given insufficient managerial scrutiny, they may lapse into inefficient operation which consumes more technical manpower than is justified. If tight administrative control is maintained, they may be brought into more appropriate balance with the result that personnel may be liberated for longer-range undertakings. Use of minor project procedures for collecting defensive work under suitable classifications points up their magnitude and thus stimulates critical review.

Operating Budgets and Accounting

Accounting serves two purposes: (1) it maintains records of all financial transactions in order to comply with good managerial practice in controlling the use of funds; (2) it provides a basis for deploying technical effort on different activities in accordance with plans. The first subject will not be discussed here, because it lies in the domain of established accounting procedures. Within the framework of such procedures, however, there is latitude for collecting financial information in the form best adapted to managerial needs.

The accounting system should be such as to conform to good practice but still afford minimum interference with the exercise of scientific and engineering talents. Excessive detail required of professional personnel in allocating charges not only becomes an irritating nuisance, but in reality does not serve a useful managerial purpose.

Use made of accounting data in programming of research and development should therefore be governed by a policy of minimum distraction from technical activities. There is an additional valid reason for this recommendation: salaries and fringe benefits of technical personnel constitute the major item of expense in laboratory and small-scale research and development. In the United States, these usually amount to nearly one-half the total departmental budget. Hence, if scientific talents are effectively distributed in the program, other items of expense will parallel this distribution. Even though technical salaries will not represent such a large percentage in countries employing lower professional/non-professional ratios and in large-scale development work, they are still the most important item in terms of contribution to the enterprise. Combined professional and non-professional salaries will in most laboratories amount to roughly two-thirds of total expense.

In earlier chapters, the use of technical time and cost data in project administration has been covered, and will not be further discussed here, except to repeat that if distribution of professional salaries is carried out, all other expenses can be distributed to projects on a prorata basis without serious distortion of individual cases, except for major items such as expensive pieces of equipment.

Professional project time, inclusive of exploratory work, will usually account for 65-75 percent of all available time in most organizations. The remainder is spent in "overhead activities," including the major categories of administration, preparation of scientific articles, participation in technical meetings and training courses, public service, vacations and holidays, and illness. It is good managerial practice to set these activities up as separate accounts, in order to provide information on the amount of professional time and associated expense devoted to each.

With a comprehensive project system, the preparation of an operating budget becomes a relatively simple procedure. If a figure has been calculated for the average total cost per man-year (either professional or professional plus non-professional), this figure multiplied by the estimated number of employees during the next budget period gives the estimated operating budget. Breakdown of the deployment of personnel according to the list of technical projects, allocations for exploratory work (which may also be described in project form), and overhead projects provides background for review by the Chief Executive in terms of willingness of the management to support this level of expenditure. Adjustment upward or downward is effected through changes in allocation of effort among the various activities. Budget preparation is therefore a synthesis of total cost of operation from estimated costs of component lines of work.

A second type of budget is also needed for both departmental administration and management review. This involves breaking down the estimated total expenditures into accounting classifications such as professional and non-professional salaries and fringe benefits, technical supplies and non-capital equipment, office supplies and expense, library, communications, travel, utilities, amortization or rental of space, and so on. Their total has been tentatively fixed by the synthesis of total cost of operation.

Once a suitable budgeting procedure has been installed, subsequent readjustment at later periods follows the same pattern. Changes are instituted in allocation of technical effort (and therefore of all associated expense) in accordance with managerial decisions.

Capital Expenditure Budgets

Many companies also prepare budgets for contemplated costs for important items of equipment or facilities in order that they may make suitable financial provision for them during the budgeting period. These are usually regarded as budget estimates and not as authorization for expenditures. Actual purchase commitments are usually made for individual items only after submission and approval of separate appropriation requests.

For technical operations, capital budget proposals usually consist of items of equipment above a prescribed minimum unit cost, major changes in facilities, and new facilities. It is customary to list the planned items of equipment, but after approval of the budget to be permitted by management to make appropriation requests for alternative items not listed. In some cases, companies will allow inclusion in the budget estimate of a sum for unanticipated items; otherwise these have to be authorized by special approval.

Purchasing for Technical Departments

In view of the fact that undue delays in obtaining equipment and materials may be very wasteful in terms of technical time, the system of procurement should be made as permissive as reasonable managerial policy will allow. Large laboratories often have a small purchasing department to expedite the ordering and receipt of their requirements.

The following are some of the restrictive procedures to be avoided insofar as possible. Central purchasing departments sometimes have the policy that all contacts with vendors must be handled by them and that all ordering must be done through standardized methods of obtaining competitive bids; a situation of this type is suitable for purchase of standardized commodities or equipment, but it often entails many difficulties when applied to specialized materials or equipment required for a technical project. Procedures for authorization of purchases may be unduly restrictive; for example, the maxima set for different echelons may be so small that much time may be spent in getting the necessary approvals for relatively small items that are urgently needed for a project. Finally, a quite low maximum may be set for classification of items of technical equipment as capital expenditures; this policy results in the necessity for securing approval of an appropriation request under the capital budget procedures, which is usually more time-consuming than purchase as an item of expense.

Library and Information Service

Reference has been made repeatedly to the resource represented by the technical literature, and to the rapid increase in volume. The importance of tapping this reservoir is great, particularly in developing countries with restricted technical resources. The reference material includes not only published information, but also that in internal files.

There is a growing interest in "information retrieval," which is becoming a highly specialized activity, often including methods for the use of computers for this purpose. Year by year the importance and difficulty of this task become greater.

Technical Directors should therefore pay close attention to the need for adequate libraries and information services to promote effective use of the literature by their personnel. In a given case, it may be much more productive and economical to improve the library than to buy an expensive piece of equipment, or even to add another technical man to the staff.

Conclusion

This syllabus has had one goal: to emphasize the importance of bringing a competent technical man into direct contact with a problem under circumstances which convince him of its importance and provide him with access to all pertinent material and assistance required at the stage in which he is involved. This should be the guiding principle in establishing administrative policies and procedures for optimum use of the invaluable asset represented by the collective scientific and engineering talents of the organization.

ABOUT THE AUTHOR

Dr. Lawrence W. Bass is a Vice President in the New York office of Arthur D. Little, Inc., an international research organization headquartered in Cambridge, Massachusetts. Before joining the company in 1952 he had held executive positions in industry for fifteen years with The Borden Company and Air Reduction Company and most recently had served as Vice President of U.S. Industrial Chemicals Company. In addition he had been on the executive staff of Mellon Institute for eight years and had spent several years in basic research at The Rockefeller Institute and abroad. At ADL he previously headed the chemical engineering group and more recently the programs in food and biology. He has been particularly active on client assignments concerned with administration of research and development, corporate planning with special reference to technical programming, and formulation of product policies.

Dr. Bass has been much involved in overseas work of the company, having headed the comprehensive industrialization projects sponsored by the U.S. foreign aid program in Egypt in 1953-54 and in Iraq in 1954-55. He is a member of the Boards of ADL Research Institute and ADL Ltd. in the United Kingdom. In the spring of 1964 he organized and headed an ADL team which conducted a three-week intensive training course in Cairo for a group of thirty-eight Egyptian technical executives on "Management of Science and Technology in Developing Economies." This course, believed to be the first of its kind, was under the auspices of the U.A.R. National Institute of Management Development and The Ford Foundation.

Dr. Bass was graduated from Yale summa cum laude in 1919 and received his Ph.D. in chemistry there in 1922. He did research in 1923-25 at the Sorbonne, the Pasteur Institute, and the University of Lille. He also studied at Tulane University and New York University School of Law.

Dr. Bass served as an advisor on military research and development during World War II and Korea and was awarded a Presidential Certificate of Merit in 1947. He has been active in many professional organizations, particularly as president of the American Institute of Chemical Engineers and the Yale Engineering Association, chairman of Engineers Joint Council, and board member of the American Chemical Society and the American Institute of Chemists. He is the author of three books and over 100 articles.